Session Three:
Speak Words of Life

...plete the following
...homework assignments:

- □ **Workbook Section**
  Speak Words of Life

- □ **Audio** teaching of
  *Building a House of Worship
  Where You Live*
  by Dr. Jack Hayford

- □ **Book**
  Winning Spiritual Warfare
  by Neil Anderson

...nue the previous
...discipleship assignments:

- □ **Daily personal devotional**
  ...Prayer
  ...**Bible Reading** (see reverse)

- □ **Prayer partnership** with a
  prayer partner or if ...
  with spouse

- □ **Regular attendanc**
  local congregation
  the Cleansing Strea
  Seminar Group

...the following
...discipleship assign...

- □ **Worship** by singi...
  during your devot...
  before a meal

- □ **Bible Reading o**
  Couples: Husban...
  second chapter t...
  Individuals: read second
  chapter out loud

Session Two:
Commit Everything to God

...plete the following
...homework assignments:

- □ **Workbook Section**
  Commit Everything to God

- □ **Book** Chapters 8-Epilogue
  The Bait of Satan
  by Dr. John Bevere

...ntinue the previous
...discipleship assignments:

- □ **Daily personal devotional**
  ...**Prayer**
  ...**Bible Reading** (see reverse)

...e following
...discipleship assignments:

- □ **Prayer partnership** with a
  prayer partner or if married
  with spouse

- □ **Regular attendance** in your
  local congregation and at
  the Cleansing Stream
  Seminar Group

Session One:
Walk in the Spirit

...plete the following
...homework assignments:

- □ **Workbook Section**
  Walk in the Spirit

- □ **Book** Chapters 1-7
  The Bait of Satan
  by Dr. John Bevere

...lement the following
...discipleship assignments:

- □ **Daily personal devotional**
  ...Prayer
  ...Bible Reading (see reverse)

> "For I know the plans I have for you," declares the Lord, "plans to prosper you and not to harm you, plans to give you a hope and a future."
>
> Jeremiah 29:11

HEALING   FREEDOM   DISCIPLESHIP

Be free to live the life God has planned for you!

Session Five:
Press Toward the Goal

Complete the following homework assignments:

- ☐ **Workbook Section**
  Press Toward the Goal

- ☐ **Book**
  Protecting Your Home from Spiritual Darkness by Chuck Pierce and Rebecca Wagner Sytsema

Continue the previous discipleship assignments:

- ☐ **Daily personal devotional**
  ...Prayer
  ...**Bible Reading** (see reverse)
- ☐ **Prayer partnership**
- ☐ **Regular attendance**
- ☐ **Worship**
- ☐ **Bible Reading out loud**
- ☐ **Daily putting on the Armor of God**
- ☐ **Fast as the Lord directs**

Add the following discipleship assignments:

- ☐ **Cleansing** – putting your house in order
- ☐ **Covering** – setting your home apart for the Lord

© Copyright 2003 Cleansing Stream Ministries

Session Four:
Enter the Cleansing Stream

Complete the following homework assignments:

- ☐ **Workbook Section**
  Enter the Cleansing Stream

- ☐ **Audio teachings of**
  Devised for Your Defeat and Prayer Loosing Sins Bondage by Dr. Jack Hayford

Continue the previous discipleship assignments:

- ☐ **Daily personal devotional**
  ...Prayer
  ...Bible Reading (see reverse)
- ☐ **Prayer partnership** with a prayer partner or if married with spouse
- ☐ **Regular attendance** in your local congregation and at the Cleansing Stream Seminar Group
- ☐ **Worship** by singing a song during your devotional and before a meal
- ☐ **Bible Reading out loud:**
  Couples: Husband reads the second chapter to wife
  Individuals: read second chapter out loud

Add the following discipleship assignments:

- ☐ **Daily putting on the Armor of God**
- ☐ **Fast as the Lord directs**

© Copyright 2003 Cleansing Stream Ministries

Session Three:
Speak Words of Life

Death and life are in the power of the tongue.
Proverbs 18:21

Devotional Bible Reading

Week One

	Devotional	Out Loud
☐ Day 1:	Romans 8	Psalm 29
☐ Day 2:	Romans 9	Psalm 30
☐ Day 3:	Romans 10	Psalm 31
☐ Day 4:	Romans 11	Psalm 32
☐ Day 5:	Romans 12	Psalm 33
☐ Day 6:	Romans 13	Psalm 34
☐ Day 7:	Romans 14	Psalm 35

Week Two

	Devotional	Out Loud
☐ Day 1:	Romans 15	Psalm 36
☐ Day 2:	Romans 16	Psalm 37
☐ Day 3:	James 1	Psalm 38
☐ Day 4:	James 2	Psalm 39
☐ Day 5:	James 3	Psalm 40
☐ Day 6:	James 4	Psalm 41
☐ Day 7:	James 5	Psalm 42

Session Two:
Commit Everything to God

Trust in the Lord with all your heart, and lean not on your own understanding; in all your ways acknowledge Him, and He will direct your paths.
Proverbs 3:5-6

Devotional Bible Reading

Week One

☐ Day 1:	John 15	Psalm 15
☐ Day 2:	John 16	Psalm 16
☐ Day 3:	John 17	Psalm 17
☐ Day 4:	John 18	Psalm 18
☐ Day 5:	John 19	Psalm 19
☐ Day 6:	John 20	Psalm 20
☐ Day 7:	John 21	Psalm 21

Week Two

☐ Day 1:	Romans 1	Psalm 22
☐ Day 2:	Romans 2	Psalm 23
☐ Day 3:	Romans 3	Psalm 24
☐ Day 4:	Romans 4	Psalm 25
☐ Day 5:	Romans 5	Psalm 26
☐ Day 6:	Romans 6	Psalm 27
☐ Day 7:	Romans 7	Psalm 28

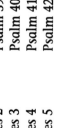
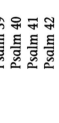
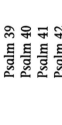
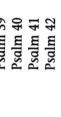

Session One:
Walk in the Spirit

If we live by the Holy Spirit, let us also walk by the Spirit. If by the Holy Spirit we have our life in God, let us go forward walking in line, our conduct controlled by the Spirit. Galatians 5:25 Amplified

Devotional Bible Reading

Week One

☐ Day 1:	John 1	Psalm 1
☐ Day 2:	John 2	Psalm 2
☐ Day 3:	John 3	Psalm 3
☐ Day 4:	John 4	Psalm 4
☐ Day 5:	John 5	Psalm 5
☐ Day 6:	John 6	Psalm 6
☐ Day 7:	John 7	Psalm 7

Week Two

☐ Day 1:	John 8	Psalm 8
☐ Day 2:	John 9	Psalm 9
☐ Day 3:	John 10	Psalm 10
☐ Day 4:	John 11	Psalm 11
☐ Day 5:	John 12	Psalm 12
☐ Day 6:	John 13	Psalm 13
☐ Day 7:	John 14	Psalm 14

Revision 11/06

Session Four:

Enter the Cleansing Stream

If we confess our sins, He is faithful and just to forgive us our sins and to cleanse us from all unrighteousness.
1 John 1:9

Devotional Bible Reading

Week One

	Devotional	*Out Loud*
☐ Day 1:	Ephesians 1	Psalm 43
☐ Day 2:	Ephesians 2	Psalm 44
☐ Day 3:	Ephesians 3	Psalm 45
☐ Day 4:	Ephesians 4	Psalm 46
☐ Day 5:	Ephesians 5	Psalm 47
☐ Day 6:	Ephesians 6	Psalm 48
☐ Day 7:	Colossians 1	Psalm 49

Week Two

	Devotional	*Out Loud*
☐ Day 1:	Colossians 2	Psalm 50
☐ Day 2:	Colossians 3	Psalm 51
☐ Day 3:	Colossians 4	Psalm 52
☐ Day 4:	2 Timothy 1	Psalm 53
☐ Day 5:	2 Timothy 2	Psalm 54
☐ Day 6:	2 Timothy 3	Psalm 55
☐ Day 7:	2 Timothy 4	Psalm 56

Session Five:

Press Toward the Goal

...forgetting what lies behind and reaching forward to what lies ahead, I press on toward the goal for the prize of the upward call of God in Christ Jesus
Philippians 3:13-14 NASB

Devotional Bible Reading

Week One

	Devotional	*Out Loud*
☐ Day 1:	Galatians 5	Psalm 57
☐ Day 2:	Hebrews 1	Psalm 58
☐ Day 3:	Hebrews 2	Psalm 59
☐ Day 4:	Hebrews 3	Psalm 60
☐ Day 5:	Hebrews 4	Psalm 61
☐ Day 6:	Hebrews 5	Psalm 62
☐ Day 7:	Hebrews 6	Psalm 63

Week Two

	Devotional	*Out Loud*
☐ Day 1:	Hebrews 7	Psalm 64
☐ Day 2:	Hebrews 8	Psalm 65
☐ Day 3:	Hebrews 9	Psalm 66
☐ Day 4:	Hebrews 10	Psalm 67
☐ Day 5:	Hebrews 11	Psalm 68
☐ Day 6:	Hebrews 12	Psalm 69
☐ Day 7:	Hebrews 13	Psalm 70

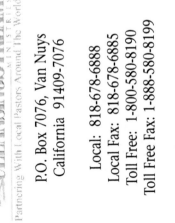

CLEANSINGSTREAM
M I N I S T R I E S
Partnering With Local Pastors Around The World

P.O. Box 7076, Van Nuys
California 91409-7076

Local: 818-678-6888
Local Fax: 818-678-6885
Toll Free: 1-800-580-8190
Toll Free Fax: 1-888-580-8199

www.cleansingstream.org

Cleansing Stream Seminar
Workbook

HEALING   **FREEDOM**   **DISCIPLESHIP**

"For I know the plans I have for you,"
declares the Lord,
"plans to prosper you and not to harm you,
plans to give you a hope and a future."

Jeremiah 29:11

Partnering With Local Pastors Around The World

Please contact us to see how we can serve you!

P.O. Box 7076, Van Nuys, California 91409-7076
Local: 818-678-6888   Local Fax: 818-678-6885
Toll Free: 1-800-580-8190   Toll Free Fax: 1-888-580-8199
www.cleansingstream.org

*And the things that you have heard from me among many witnesses,
commit these to faithful men who will be able to teach others also.* 2 Timothy 2:2

Cleansing Stream Ministries is committed to partnering
with pastors and churches in teaching and training
leaders and maturing believers
in personal cleansing, deliverance, and spiritual warfare
so they can be released to serve, minister, and disciple
others in the Body of Christ.

———————————

Cleansing Stream Ministries is committed to and under the covering of
the Cleansing Stream Ministries Board and The Church On The Way in Van Nuys,
California with Dr. Jack Hayford, Founding Pastor.

Unless otherwise indicated, all Scripture quotations are from *The Holy Bible*, New King James Version (NKJV).
Copyright © 1979, 1980, 1982 by Thomas Nelson, Inc. Used by permission. All rights reserved.

Scripture quotations marked NIV are taken from *The Holy Bible*, New International Version (NIV).
Copyright © 1973, 1978, 1984 by the International Bible Society. Used by permission of Zondervan Publishing
House. All rights reserved.

Scripture quotations marked NLT are taken from *The Holy Bible*, New Living Translation (NLT).
Copyright © 1986 by Tyndale House Publishers, Wheaton, Illinois, 60189. Used by permission. All rights
reserved.

Scripture quotations marked NASB are taken from *The Holy Bible*, New American Standard Bible (NASB).
Copyright © 1960, 1962, 1963, 1968, 1971, 1972, 1973, 1975, 1977, 1995 by the Lockman Foundation. Used
by permission. All rights reserved.

A special thanks to Descanso Gardens in the City of Flintridge-La Cañada for use of their location.

Contact Cleansing Stream Ministries for further information.

By phone:
Toll free number 800-580-8190
Local number 818-678-6888

By mail:
P.O. Box 7076
Van Nuys, California 91409-7076

Or visit our website: www.cleansingstream.org

Table of Contents

Dear Friend,

There can be no greater privilege—nor challenge—than preparing oneself for useful service to Jesus Christ. As with the apostle Paul, we have sometimes said,

For to will is present with me, but how to perform what is good I do not find. Romans 7:18

Yet, just a few verses later he states,

I thank God— through Jesus Christ our Lord!

It is with this hope and expectation that you now journey toward the Cleansing Stream. All trails have their ups and downs, their twists and turns; it is what makes any walk interesting. You may enter into some new territory, or you may find the terrain quite familiar. Either way, the Holy Spirit, who is your helper and guide, will accompany you all the way. You are not alone!

Of course, your journey will last a lifetime. This walk you and I are on, will not find its ultimate destination until we arrive in Heaven. But I am thankful that for this particular portion of time we can partner together with you.

I can offer no greater prayer for you than this:

That He would grant you, according to the riches of His glory, to be strengthened with might through His Spirit in the inner man, that Christ may dwell in your hearts through faith; that you, being rooted and grounded in love may be able to comprehend with all the saints what is the width and length and depth and height—to know the love of Christ which passes knowledge; that you may be filled with all the fullness of God. Ephesians 3:16-19

With Prayerful Anticipation,

Pastor Chris Hayward
President, Cleansing Stream Ministries

About the Seminar

"For I know the plans I have for you," declares the Lord,
"plans to prosper you and not to harm you,
plans to give you a **hope** *and a* **future**.*" *Jeremiah 29:11 (NIV)*

As the Lord revealed Jeremiah 29:11 to be the theme verse for the New Cleansing Stream Seminar, excitement began to stir in our hearts! Often we forget that God has plans for us and for our lives plans full of hope that provide a wonderful future. Often we are distracted by our current circumstances and become discouraged and lose heart. We believe this Seminar will help you to refocus, set things in order, regain hope and get a true perspective of your future.

The Cleansing Stream Seminar is *more* than just the teachings. It is *more* than the workbook, *more* than the Discipleship Assignments, *more* than the homework (books and audio teachings), *more* than the small group meetings and the relationships cultivated, *more* than the Retreat and the ministry of healing and freedom received. The Cleansing Stream Seminar and Retreat is more than just the sum of its parts. You have heard the expression, "The **whole** is more than the **sum of the parts**" that perfectly describes the Seminar!

Our Father desires for us to be planted and to grow into all that He created us to be. Participating in the Cleansing Stream Seminar and Retreat will be an avenue the Lord will use in this restoration process, establishing your roots as He nurtures, prunes, and matures you in righteousness for His glory.

Committing to let God work in your life involves extending yourself—setting aside your time and resources and being willing to be transparent by sharing your challenges so that others can pray with and support you. So commit to do it all!

We are so excited about your commitment. We believe the Lord has much in store for you! Expect healing, freedom and discipleship! Expect hope to be restored and an anticipation of the future to be ignited. May you join with so many others who have testified:

"God has used this to change my life forever!"

About the Workbook

This Workbook has been created to compliment the Cleansing Stream Session teachings. As you progress through the Seminar you will be digging deeper into the Word of God. Though this workbook is not an exhaustive study, it will provide you with foundational Biblical truths as well as their practical applications. This is just **one piece** of the **whole**. But together this workbook and the other pieces of the Seminar will be used by the Lord to prepare your heart and mind and strengthen your will for what He will do in you at the Retreat and beyond!

As you begin you will need the following...

A willing heart

> *Search me, O God, and know my heart; test me...* Psalm 139:23 (NIV)

Be willing, be open to the Lord and His work in your life. Whether it be—encouragement, discipleship, correction or just words of love, commit now to be willing to take it in, to see it, to act on it!

A prayerful attitude

> *But when He, the Spirit of Truth, comes, He will guide you into all truth.* John 16:13 (NIV)

Ask the Holy Spirit to teach you! The Holy Spirit is the Teacher of the Church, so we must submit our hearts to Him and ask for His enlightenment and revelation as we study the Word—and we do that through prayer. It doesn't have to be impressive or eloquent, just a humble heart asking for God's help. For example, "Lord, as I spend time in Your Word, help me to know You better."

Your tools

Your Bible, your workbook, a pen or a pencil

Here are some helpful hints for how to utilize this workbook...

Try to complete one section of the Session assigned each time you sit down.

> *Oh, how I love your law! I meditate on it all day long.* Psalm 119:97 (NIV)

Each Session is divided into sections of about 2-3 pages. Each Session ends with journal and a prayer commitment pages. Whenever possible, complete an entire section in one sitting. This will help you focus on the specific concept being presented.

Use the "Notes" column on each page for recording ideas and questions that come up so that you can refer back to them later.

Speaking the truth in love, we will in all things grow up into him who is the Head, that is, Christ. Ephesians 4:15 (NIV)

The Lord will speak to you as you study His Word, so be ready to write it down! Ideas will come to mind. Bible verses will stand out. Questions will surface. Write these things down so that you can remember them to share them as you meet with your Cleansing stream Seminar group.

Session One:
Walk in the Spirit

*If we live by the Holy Spirit,
let us also walk by the Spirit.
If by the Holy Spirit we have our life in God,
let us go forward, walking in line,
our conduct controlled by the Spirit.*

Galatians 5:25 (Amplified)

Session One:

Walk in the Spirit

Complete the following
homework assignments:

☐ **Workbook Section**
Walk in the Spirit

☐ **Book** Chapters 1-7
The Bait of Satan
by Dr. John Bevere

Implement the following
discipleship assignments:

☐ **Daily personal devotional**
...**Prayer**
...**Bible Reading** (see reverse)

© Copyright 2003 Cleansing Stream Ministries

Session One:

Walk in the Spirit

*If we live by the Holy Spirit, let us also walk by
the Spirit. If by the Holy Spirit we have our life in God,
let us go forward walking in line, our conduct controlled
by the Spirit.* Galatians 5:25 Amplified

Devotional Bible Reading

Week One

☐	Day 1:	John 1	Psalm 1
☐	Day 2:	John 2	Psalm 2
☐	Day 3:	John 3	Psalm 3
☐	Day 4:	John 4	Psalm 4
☐	Day 5:	John 5	Psalm 5
☐	Day 6:	John 6	Psalm 6
☐	Day 7:	John 7	Psalm 7

Week Two

☐	Day 1:	John 8	Psalm 8
☐	Day 2:	John 9	Psalm 9
☐	Day 3:	John 10	Psalm 10
☐	Day 4:	John 11	Psalm 11
☐	Day 5:	John 12	Psalm 12
☐	Day 6:	John 13	Psalm 13
☐	Day 7:	John 14	Psalm 14

Revision 11/06

About the Discipleship Assignment

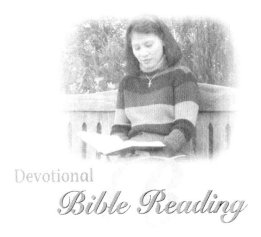

Devotional
Bible Reading

God's Word, His character, His will and ways are so amazing, how will we ever be able to fully understand them? Praise the Lord it is a journey! Today the Lord is calling you to *Walk in the Spirit*. For some it will be another step in a journey you began long ago, for others it will be the beginning. Whichever it is, the Lord desires to meet you in your personal devotional time of Bible reading and prayer.

Why Daily Personal Bible Reading?

- □ Psalm 119:105 tells you that God's Word is a lamp to your feet

- □ God's Word is one way for you to know Him—His character and ways AND to be known by Him—it is essential to your relationship and intimacy!

How do you implement it?

- □ First, with expectation, ask the Lord to make our devotional reading—a time for personal insight and a time of revelation about yourself.

- □ Second, try these practical tips:

  - Try a modern version of the Bible, different than the one usually used.

  - Next, ask the Lord to stimulate faith, direct and correct through the Word that is read.

  - Then underline or write in the margins what He reveals!

- □ Third, get started by following the daily Bible Reading Assignment.

About the Discipleship Assignment

Devotional
Prayer

Why Daily Personal Prayer?

☐ Isn't your prayer like that of David's in Psalm 25:4-5? **SHOW** *me Your ways, O Lord;* **TEACH** *me Your paths.* **LEAD** *me in Your truth and teach me, for You are the God of my salvation; on You I wait all the day.*

☐ Prayer is another way to know *Him, His way, His path,* and *His truth!*

☐ Prayer is an invitation for Him to SHOW, TEACH, and LEAD you!

How do you implement it?

☐ Do it daily!

☐ There is a basic path for personal prayer you can follow. Jesus taught His disciples in Matthew 6:9-13. Just remember P R A Y E R!

P raise the Lord for He is worthy! *Our Father in Heaven, Hallowed be Your name.*

R epent of sin that is in the way of your relationship with Him. *And forgive us our debts, as we forgive our debtors.*

A sk the Lord for physical and spiritual provision. *Give us this day our daily bread. And do not lead us into temptation, but deliver us from the evil one.*

Y ield to His will and His plans! *Your kingdom come. Your will be done...*

E xpand your vision—pray for your family and friends, city, country, the world. *On earth as it is in heaven.*

R ecognize and declare that His *...is the kingdom and the power and the glory forever. Amen.*

These two daily personal devotional disciplines are so important—talking to Him and letting Him speak to you—is at the very heart of intimacy! As a result we know that God will create in us a hunger for more of Him, a passion to be what He wants us to become and a humility and dependency on Him! We are excited about the path you are on today! God Bless you as you go.

During the Teaching

What does it mean to *Walk* in the Spirit?

Scriptures

Therefore take up the whole armor of God, that you may be able to withstand in the evil day, and having done all, to stand. Ephesians 6:13

If we live in the Spirit, let us also walk in the Spirit. Galatians 5:25

(Take up your cross) Matthew 16:24

(Give us our daily bread) Matthew 6:11

Theme Scripture:

If we live by the Holy Spirit, let us also WALK by the Spirit. If by the Holy Spirit we have our life in God, let us go forward, walking in line, our conduct controlled by the Spirit. Galatians 5:25 (Amplified)

Definition:

"Walk" to move with...

> *Purpose*—our conduct pleasing to the Lord
> *Observation*—watching for distractions, obstacles, assaults
> *Balance*—going forward with discernment, determination
> *Action*—step-by-step, decision-by-decision, choice-by-choice

Quotes

What does it mean to *Walk* in the Spirit?

Spirit... Soul... Body

Scriptures

Now may the God of peace Himself sanctify you completely; and may your whole spirit, soul, and body be preserved blameless at the coming of our Lord Jesus Christ. 1 Thessalonians 5:23

Who delivered us from so great a death, and does deliver us; in whom we trust that He will still deliver us. 2 Corinthians 1:10

...that you may be able to withstand in the evil day... Ephesians 6:13

For by one offering He has perfected forever those who are being sanctified. Hebrews 10:14

Quotes

Justification—
    Spirit—*instantly*

Sanctification—
    Soul—*ongoing process*

"Being secure in my justification gives me the freedom to work and cooperate with God in my sanctification."

What does it mean to *Walk* in the Spirit?

For the flesh lusts against the Spirit, and the Spirit against the flesh; and these are contrary to one another, so that you do not do the things that you wish. Galatians 5:17

Flesh vs. Spirit

Quotes

"The **flesh** is the **soul unsurrendered**—your *mind*—thoughts not renewed; your *emotions*—desires not submitted to God; your *will*—choices not Spirit-led. And your *body*—undisciplined."

"The spiritual person is one who quickly surrenders and keeps walking in the Spirit."

What does it mean to walk in the Spirit?

It means to walk spiritually with *purpose, balance, observation* and *action, keeping your eyes* on Jesus and *winning the tug of war* to be led by the Holy Spirit rather than allowing your soul to rule over your choices and decisions. Walking in the Spirit is the process of your soul learning to relinquish control and let God take charge of your life. Always remember, you are His work in process!

Why *Walk* in the Spirit?

Intimacy... Power... Destiny

Scriptures

My sheep hear My voice...
John 10:27

Finally, my brethren, be strong in the Lord and in the power of His might. Ephesians 6:10

...that you may be able to withstand in the evil day...
Ephesians 6:13

Above all, taking the shield of faith with which you will be able to quench all the fiery darts of the wicked one.
Ephesians 6:16

For which I am an ambassador in chains; that in it I may speak boldly, as I ought to speak. Ephesians 6:20

"For I know the thoughts that I think toward you," says the Lord, *"thoughts of peace and not of evil, to give you a future and a hope."* Jeremiah 29:11

Quotes

"When we contend with the flesh we are self-focused. When we are walking in the Spirit we are Christ-centered."

Why walk in the Spirit?

Walking in the Spirit allows you to experience *intimacy* with the Lord, which releases His *power* in your life so that you can fulfill your *destiny* in Christ.

How do you *Walk* in the Spirit?

See then that you walk circumspectly, not as fools but as wise. Ephesians 5:15

Circumspectly—Vigilant... Watchful

Quotes

"We walk in rank, with our eyes fixed on Jesus and our ears attentive to our Commander's voice."

How do you *Walk* in the Spirit?

Scriptures

(Pray for your enemies)
Matthew 5:44-45

Step-by-step—with Praise and Thanksgiving

Quotes

"We need to turn our focus to praise and thanksgiving to God for who He is— trusting in God's Word, believing in His character— choosing not to let our soul dominate—that way we can overcome the flesh."

How do you walk in the Spirit?

You walk in the Spirit daily, *circumspectly* (watchful and vigilant), *step-by-step*, listening for His voice, with purpose and thanksgiving! Daily choosing to follow the leading of the Holy Spirit instead of the desires of your flesh.

In Summary:

What does it mean to walk in the Spirit?

It means to walk spiritually with *purpose, balance, observation* and *action, keeping your eyes* on Jesus and *winning the tug of war* to be led by the Holy Spirit rather than allowing your soul to rule over your choices and decisions. Walking in the Spirit is the process of your soul learning to relinquish control and let God take charge of your life. Always remember, you are His work in process!

Why walk in the Spirit?

Walking in the Spirit allows you to experience *intimacy* with the Lord, which releases His *power* in your life so that you can fulfill your *destiny* in Christ.

How do you walk in the Spirit?

You walk in the Spirit daily, *circumspectly* (watchful and vigilant), *step-by-step,* listening for His voice, with purpose and thanksgiving! Daily choosing to follow the leading of the Holy Spirit instead of the desires of your flesh.

Further Study

What does it mean to

Walk in the Spirit?

Introduction

Walking in the Spirit is not like any other journey you have ever taken. It is a walk of restoration and blessing, a walk of intimacy and power. Having submitted your life to the Lordship of Jesus Christ, His Spirit made you spiritually alive, and all the power and purpose of the kingdom of God now dwells inside of you. In order to experience the fullness of this blessing, you must learn to walk with Him *in the Spirit,* daily, decision-by-decision.

In this session we will be answering three main questions.

□ *What* does it means to walk in the Spirit?

□ *Why* walk in the Spirit?

□ *How* do you walk in the Spirit?

The key verse for this session is Galatians 5:25. Write it out below and then dive in. May God's peace and grace be with you as you seek to know Him!

Galatians 5:25

1.1 Walk Defined

Every walk has a purpose or destination. It may be a casual walk to drink in the pleasure of a few leisurely moments. It may be a hurried walk to reach an appointed destination on time. Or it may be a regimented exercise to keep your mind and body alert and healthy. Whatever the goal, the method is the same: you put one foot in front of the other. To reach your goal requires that you stay on the right path and avoid any distractions or hindrances along the way. Walking is a step-by-step process that requires observation and steady balance.

Walking in the Spirit is much like taking a physical walk and incorporates the same elements. *Remember...*

Walking in the Spirit Requires...	
Purpose	Keeping your eyes fixed on Jesus
Observation	Being vigilant and watchful
Balance	Being discerning and determined
Action	Being led by the Spirit instead of allowing your soul to rule

God has set a wonderful path in front of you, and He wants to see you reach the end while enjoying the journey. To do that, you must learn to walk in step with the Holy Spirit, with purpose, observation and balance on His pathway—one step at a time.

You are embarking on that journey right now. For some this will be another step in a journey you began long ago, for others it will be the beginning. Whatever the case, if you will put into practice the truths presented throughout the Cleansing Stream Seminar Sessions and implement the Discipleship Assignments into your everyday life, then you will journey into a place of spiritual release and victory.

Write out what you would like to see God do for you as you journey through the Cleansing Stream Seminar and attend the Retreat.

Then spend a few moments in prayer sharing your desires and asking for His will to be accomplished.

Think of a troop of soldiers. They hold rank and march in full submission and obedience to their leader, turning quickly at each command. Walking in the Spirit means that you learn to quickly move at God's Word, yielding to the direction and guidance of your Commander-in-Chief.

How do you do this? How do you walk in the Spirit? It begins by understanding who you are and how God made you.

1.2 Understand How You Are Made

You are so much more than just your name, your physical features, or your heritage. You have been created by God to reflect His image; you have been redeemed by Him to be a part of His family and to walk in the power of His Spirit. Understanding this will set you on the path that leads to victory.

First Thessalonians 5:23 says "Now may the God of peace Himself sanctify you completely; and may your whole spirit, soul, and body be preserved blameless at the coming of our Lord Jesus Christ."

Circle the words "spirit," "soul" and "body."

Often it is explained in these terms: I am a spiritual being, I have a soul and I live in a body. Let's break each part of that phrase down in light of the Scriptures.

I am a Spiritual Being

As you read the following scriptures, note what they show about you as a "spiritual being."

☐ Genesis 1:27; 2:7

☐ John 4:24

The Bible says that God created man in His image. But what exactly does that mean? Did Adam look like God? What about Eve? The answer is yes—but not in their physical characteristics, such as hair and eye color or nose shape. Adam and Eve were created as spiritual beings with characteristics like their Father, God. After Adam and Eve were created, God breathed into them and they became living beings. The Hebrew word for "breath" in this verse is the same word used elsewhere for "spirit." God is spirit. So God brought them to life with His own breath, His own Spirit. You are first of all, a *spiritual* being. You were made *like* Him so that you could enjoy a relationship *with* Him. For intimacy with Him, you had to be like Him—a spiritual being. Your spirit is the part of you that communes with Him and will live forever.

I Have a Soul

As you read the following scriptures, note what they show about your "soul."

☐ Psalm 103:1

☐ Matthew 22:37

Though in essence you are a spiritual being, God gave you a soul, too. In fact, Jesus says to love God with, among other things, "all your soul." Your **soul** can be defined as your *mind*—what you think, your *emotions*— what you feel and your *will*—what you choose to do. Through your soul, you relate to the people and the world around you. Because your soul is where you make your choices, this is the part of your being that must be continually brought under the leadership of the Lord. What you think, what you feel and what you choose to do, can either draw you closer to God or move you further from Him. Thus, the soul is the primary battlefield as you learn to walk in the Spirit.

I Live in a Body

As you read the following scriptures, note what they show about your "body."

☐ Romans 12:1

☐ 1 Corinthians 6:19-20

Though most people tend to think of themselves based on what they look like on the outside, the physical part of their being is the least of what makes them "them." In reality, bodies are only temporary housing. It is important, however, that as a Christian you use your body to honor God. This means that you choose to live a holy and respectable life, walking by the leading of the Spirit not by the leading of your body or your soul. The Bible is clear that one day we will put aside our earthly body for a heavenly body.

Philippians 3:20-21 tell us that "...our citizenship is in heaven, from which we also eagerly wait for the Savior, the Lord Jesus Christ, who will transform our lowly body that it may be conformed to His glorious body, according to the working by which He is able even to subdue all things to Himself."

Stop and thank God for His transforming power!

So, what does all this have to do with walking in the Spirit? Because of how God made people, walking in the Spirit is a learning process. *Remember...*

Your...	Before Salvation	After Salvation *(See Appendix page 5-38)*
Spirit	Dead because of sin	Alive through the power of the Holy Spirit
Soul	Self-focused	Now must learn to submit to God
Body	Undisciplined	Now must be disciplined

Before you received Christ, your spirit was dead because of sin. Remember that you were created as a spiritual being and were designed to relate to God through your spirit. Sin disconnected you from Him. To compensate, you learned to let your soul be in charge—choosing whatever you thought or felt was best—to get you through life. The problem with this method is before Christ, your soul was self-focused. This led to choices that were not always best and many of which went against God's Word.

Read Romans 1:29-31; 8:7. What were you like apart from Christ (before you were saved)?

Read Ephesians 2:1,5 and Colossians 2:13. Describe what happened to you when you received salvation.

When you were born again, God made you spiritually alive, and now you can choose to be led by Him. Walking in the Spirit is the process of your soul learning to relinquish control and let God take charge of your life.

Do you remember the illustration of the husband coming home after being gone for many years during the War? Though his wife was glad for his safe return and happy to submit to his headship in their home, it was not an instant transition. During the years he was away, she had learned, by necessity, to be self-sufficient and releasing that control was a step-by-step, and sometimes challenging decision.

No doubt you are likewise glad that God redeemed you and now resides with you. However, the process of *submitting* your thoughts and feelings and *surrendering* your choices to His headship happens daily—choice-by-choice.

In which area of your life do you feel the most self-sufficient?

Stop and tell the Lord you want to learn to follow His lead in that area.

Remember the military example? When the soldiers first arrived at boot camp, they knew nothing about being a soldier. It was only after intense training that they walked and acted in a manner that let everyone who saw them know who they were. The same is true for you. God's Spirit has made you alive again. Now it's time to get trained by His Spirit so that everyone who sees you will know that you are a child of God—you belong to Him!

1.3 Learning to Obey the Signals

What does all this have to do with learning to walk in the Spirit? When God saved you, He made your spirit alive, but your soul—your mind, emotions and will—must be continually reminded to submit to and obey His Word and the Holy Spirit. This simply means that you are a work in progress. God is changing you to be more like Him every time you submit your soul to Him. You are *completely* saved yet *continually* sanctified!

Hebrews 10:14 says, "For by one offering He has perfected forever those who are being sanctified."

Underline the phrase "perfected forever" and circle the phrase "are being sanctified."

When you accepted the Lord, He saved you and justified you. Right at that moment, you were "perfected forever" in the sense that you were forgiven of your sins and declared "not guilty" in His eyes (see Romans 5:1). **Justification** happened *instantly,* at that moment, when God made you spiritually alive. **Sanctification** began at that moment, too, but it is a *process* that continues while we live on this earth. Sanctification has to do with bringing your *soul* under His authority, daily learning to make choices that please and honor Him.

To summarize…

God's Work	Where?	How?	What?
Justification	Spirit	Instantly occurred the moment you were saved	The record of Jesus is applied to you and it is as if you never sinned
Sanctification	Soul	Ongoing process of surrendering your soul	The cooperation with the work of the Holy Spirit

Go back to Hebrew 10:14. Write "justification" or "sanctification" next to the appropriate phrase.

Think about the three lights of an ordinary traffic signal and how they relate to walking in the Spirit. The green light is like your body. It screams "Go! Go! Go!" to everything that feels good, whether it is good or destructive. The yellow light is like your soul; it is more cautious—it slows you down to see how you think or feel. But the red light is like your spirit because it says, "Stop and listen for the Lord's direction." Walking in the Spirit means that you learn to stop, like the red light. There the Lord is waiting to guide you on your path. Yet the point of decision is in your soul. Will your soul relate to God through your spirit—stopping to listen and discern, then making the decision to do what He says, or will you go where you please, when you please in order to satisfy your flesh?

Read Galatians 5:17. How does this verse describe the idea of a tug-of-war between spirit and flesh (i.e., the desires of the soul and body not yet submitted to His control)?

This tug of war of choosing between your flesh and spirit is a part of the ongoing process of sanctification in our lives. As you continue to submit your soul—how you think, feel and choose—to the Lord, obeying His Word and Spirit, you will find the power to say *no* to ungodliness and *yes* to His commands.

Can you begin to see why there is a struggle? Though you have been saved, giving up control is difficult. There is an ongoing tug-of-war in which your spirit is pulling you to follow God's instructions and the Holy Spirit, while the desires of your not-yet-submitted flesh (sometimes encouraged by the enemy) is crying out to gratify its selfish desires. Either way, you are faced with a decision: Will you choose to walk in the Spirit or to walk as you see fit?

In the teaching you heard the statement, "Being secure in my justification, I am now free to cooperate with God in my sanctification." God is working in you to bring you to complete freedom and wholeness. It is a process, but one in which you can be assured the victory as long as you stick close to Him.

Read Philippians 1:6. How does knowing you are justified help you be patient as you become sanctified?

What does it mean to walk in the Spirit?

It means to walk spiritually with *purpose, balance, observation* and *action, keeping your eyes on Jesus* and *winning the tug of war* to be led by the Holy Spirit rather than allowing your soul to rule over your choices and decisions. Walking in the Spirit is the process of your soul learning to relinquish control and letting God take charge of your life. Always remember, you are His work in process!

Why

Walk in the Spirit?

2.1 Intimacy... Power... Destiny

Intimacy

Knowing that God made us in His image, we can begin to understand the purpose of learning to walk in the Spirit. He designed us for intimate fellowship with Him. God's idea was not to create life and then watch it from a distance. No, He loves His creation beyond what words can express and desires to be involved in their lives every minute of every day. By bringing your soul under His Lordship and choosing to obey His Word, you keep in step with Him and enjoy rich intimacy and fellowship.

Read the following scriptures and describe the way to know the Lord and have intimacy with Him.

☐ Matthew 11:27

☐ John 17:25-26

God loves you with the same love with which He loves His own Son, Jesus. Think about that for a minute. Doesn't it send shivers up your spine? God loves *you*. And it isn't a barely-tolerate-because-I-have-to love, it is a completely over-the-top, can't-get-enough-of-you kind of love. Amazing? *Yes.* Unbelievable? *Definitely.* True? *Absolutely!*

Read Ephesians 1:17; 3:14-21. What does the writer ask the Father to give the believers at Ephesus?

God's primary joy is not our productivity, but our willingness to spend time in His presence—not in strict discipline, but in loving fellowship. As a follower of Jesus, He has given you His Spirit to lead you into intimacy with the Father. God does not want you to live life on your own. He means for you to come back into close union with Him and that happens as you walk in the Spirit.

Power

From that place of intimate fellowship with the Lord, you find strength to fight the spiritual battles—from the struggle with an unsurrendered desire to an attack of the enemy—that assault you every day. As you walk in the Spirit, you can discipline your flesh and be empowered to enforce the victory Jesus won on the cross against the enemy.

Second Timothy 1:7 says, "For God has not given us a spirit of fear, but of power and of love and of a sound mind."

Circle what the Lord has given you.

How does this give you confidence and power as you face a spiritual battle?

What power do you have against the enemy? All the power of God Himself! You face Satan clothed in the same power that raised Jesus from the dead!

Read Ephesians 6:10-18. According to verse 10, what is the source of our strength and power?

According to verse 13, what will you be able to do as you wear the armor of God?

How does this give you confidence to stand against the enemy?

Read Hebrews 4:12. The Word is like a sword. Fill in the following chart noting what it can divide between.

Divides between...		
	and	
	and	
	and	

In light of these passages, can you see how the Spirit gives you the power to overcome your flesh and the enemy? The Holy Spirit takes the Word of God and uses it to discern between *your soulish* thoughts, feelings and actions and *His Spirit* or even *the enemy*. As you pick up the Word, you pick up a mighty and powerful sword that can cut through confusion and turmoil and tell the difference between flesh and spirit.

Destiny

Right along with intimacy and power, walking in the Spirit allows God to restore His purpose for your life. You are a uniquely crafted, one-of-a-kind creation made to know and enjoy your Creator. Walking in the Spirit enables you to fulfill your God-ordained purpose and see God's plans for your life released.

Read the following scriptures and note what they say about the plans and thoughts God has for you.

☐ Psalm 139:16

☐ Jeremiah 29:11-13 *Write this one out, inserting your name each place "you" appears.*

The *New International Version* uses the word "plans." Often "plans" are described as the achievements that you may or may not accomplish; however, God's plans for you do not center on what you can achieve. Rather, His plans center on your relationship with Him. He wants you to know Him. Remember that the purpose of your life is fellowship with God. Yes, He has specific plans for your future—good and wonderful plans. But the key to your destiny is an ongoing dependence and obedience that keeps you in step with His Spirit.

Why walk in the Spirit?

Walking in the Spirit allows you to experience *intimacy* with the Lord, which releases His *power* in your life so that you can fulfill your *destiny* in Christ.

How do you

Walk in the Spirit?

3.1 Circumspectly

Ephesians 5:15 says, "See then that you walk circumspectly, not as fools but as wise."

Walking in the Spirit involves walking circumspectly. This means that you walk with watchfulness or vigilance. When you take a walk through potentially difficult terrain, you keep your eyes wide open and your body ready to act. Likewise, as you seek to walk in the Spirit, you must keep your heart and mind attentive to the direction of the Lord so that you can act when He leads.

What you choose to look at will determine where you end up. Nowhere is this more important than in the Christian walk. You must keep your focus upon Jesus if you are going to run this race well. As you fix your gaze upon Him, He gives you the strength, wisdom and ability to obey His direction and continue on the path.

As you read the following scriptures, underline where you are to look.

Hebrews 12:2-3 (NIV) "Let us fix our eyes on Jesus, the author and perfecter of our faith, who for the joy set before him endured the cross, scorning its shame, and sat down at the right hand of the throne of God. Consider him who endured such opposition from sinful men, so that you will not grow weary and lose heart."

Psalm 141:8 (NIV) "But my eyes are fixed on you, O Sovereign Lord; in you I take refuge-do not give me over to death."

Although the writer of this psalm was specifically referring to being saved from physical death, there is an important truth that applies to your walk with the Lord. Death to your joys, hopes, dreams and desires happen when you cease to keep your gaze upon the Sovereign One Who can do the impossible. To walk in the Spirit, you must keep your eyes fixed on the Lord. As you do, you will gain strength and wisdom, which will enable you to obey, wisely choosing your attitudes, words and actions.

You are able to see the Lord through His Word and through time spent with Him. Your Discipleship Assignments for this session are daily, personal devotional Bible reading and prayer. The Bible is the written revelation that God has given you to know Him. This is why daily Bible reading is an essential part of your Christian walk. To read the Word is to look at God and His ways. To pray is a chance to speak to the Lord and let Him speak to you.

He chooses to reveal Himself through His Word and through conversation in prayer. You will come to see Him as a loving Savior who laid down His life to bring the world salvation. You will see a strong King who can decree His will and have it come to pass. You will see a good Shepherd who diligently and watchfully guides us as we step along the path.

Remember...

Walking in the Spirit Requires...	
Purpose	Keeping your eyes fixed on Jesus
Observation	Being vigilant and watchful
Balance	Being discerning and determined
Action	Being led by the Spirit instead of allowing your soul to rule

3.2 Step-by-Step

The keys to walking in the Spirit are dependence and obedience. To depend on someone is to place your trust in them, to believe that they will do what they say and to trust that what they ask you to do will be for your good. In your walk with God, you must lay your life before Him in ongoing trust and reliance and obey Him—choice-by-choice...step-by-step.

Read 2 Chronicles 16:9a. What kind of people is God looking for?

What does He promise to do for them?

It is easy to continue to trust the Lord when things are going well. But eventually you will come upon some rocky terrain. It is in these times of turmoil that your choice to continue to depend on God and obey Him is critical.

Galatians 5:25 (Amplified) says, "If we live by the Holy Spirit, let us also walk by the Spirit. If by the Holy Spirit we have our life in God, let us go forward walking in line, our conduct controlled by the Spirit."

What does it mean to you to "keep in step with the Spirit?"

As you walk in the Spirit, distractions, obstacles and assaults can get in your way. In the teaching, you were given several examples of each type of potential challenge. In those examples you could see how the flesh (sometimes aided by the enemy) could pull you away from your spirit. But you could also see how your spirit (prompted by the Holy Spirit), could see the truth, overcome and walk in the Spirit.

Remember...

Type of Challenge	Explanation	Example
Distractions	Things that pull you away from walking in the Spirit	Cares of this life: bills, rebellious children, health
Obstacles	Things that get in the way of you walking in the Spirit	Offenses: someone says something against you
Assaults	The enemy's attack to keep you from walking in the Spirit	Spiritual warfare: doubt and unbelief, lies of the enemy

You have experienced this tug of war between your flesh and spirit. Write down an area of challenge—distraction, obstacle, or assault—to your walk in the Spirit.

What is the source—your flesh (thoughts or feelings) or the enemy?

What is the truth about this area? (What does God's Word say about it? Write down one scripture.)

Ask the Lord to help you believe this truth and overcome the distraction, obstacle, or assault so you can make the choice to walk in the Spirit. Declare the truth aloud to set you back on the path!

The Bible says that believers will experience trouble. Either the devil will assault you, or hurt and offense may become an obstacle in your life, or you could just quit pursuing Jesus because of distractions. The common remedy for each of the challenges that come your way is simple: keep your eyes on Jesus; continue to trust in His Word and His Spirit; believe in His perfect character; and walk circumspectly before Him. By walking in the Spirit choice-by-choice and focusing on the Lord, you can successfully stay on your path and complete your journey.

3.3 Listen for His Voice

Have you ever played the childhood game where one person is blindfolded and the others call out directions to guide the one who cannot see to a specific place? What is the first thing the blindfolded person does? They listen intently for a familiar voice to trust and follow. Zeroing in on that voice, they try to block out all the other shouts and noise so that their dependable guide can give them the right directions. As they obey the instructions, they can reach their destination.

What a great picture of how you can rise above the noise of your flesh and the enemy that shouts false direction to your souls and hear the One who can guide you to the other side in safety. Because you belong to Him, you can learn to hear His voice and enjoy a life lived under his guidance and protection.

Read John 10:4. Why do the sheep follow the Shepherd?

As you learn to walk in the Spirit, with watchfulness and vigilance, daily depending on the Lord and keeping in step with Him through obedience, you may make mistakes. The good news is that God does not condemn you. In fact, the Bible makes it clear that there is *no condemnation* for those who are in Christ Jesus (see Romans 8:1).

Just like a child who falls, you can get right back up and continue to take the steps you know you are to take, trusting your Good Shepherd. How do you get back up? By repenting and asking for His forgiveness. It is as simple as that. Then, through dependence and obedience, you can get back on the path of walking in the Spirit!

Hearing the Lord does not necessarily mean that you audibly hear a voice speak. The majority of the time, hearing the Lord means His Spirit is guiding you through the Word, through others, and/or through your thoughts and desires as they are submitted to Him.

You can learn to recognize the voice of the Lord when you are able to quiet your soul. He speaks to your spirit by His Spirit, and it always lines up with His Word.

Look up the following verses and briefly note what they say about listening to the Lord.

☐ Isaiah 30:21

☐ Revelation 3:20

If you are going to walk in the Spirit, you must learn to stop and listen for His direction. Let the clamor of the world be silenced by filling your mind and heart with His Word. When you begin a conversation, when you commit to an activity—at every point of choice—stop and ask for God's guidance. He will answer you—you can count in it.

List an area of your life that could use more direction from the Lord.

Tell Him you need His help—then expect Him to direct you!

3.4 With Purpose and Thanksgiving

To conclude this session, the truth of the Word has been planted deeply into your heart. Walking in the Spirit is all about an ongoing surrender to the Lord and His ways. You seek Him by His Spirit, submit to His Word, and decide daily—in fact, choice-by-choice—to obey Him and live in a way that honors and glorifies Him.

Read 1 Corinthians 16:13-14. List the five commands given in these verses.

    1.

    2.

    3.

    4.

    5.

To successfully walk in the Spirit, you must be alert and determined. It is not always an easy walk, but it is always worth the effort! You must look past the distractions, obstacles and assaults that will come your way, and, with the help of the Holy Spirit, choose to obey and act in a manner that pleases your Heavenly Father. Remember, that He is *in* you to work His will *through* you (see Philippians 2:13, NLT). You are not alone!

Read the following scriptures. On what are you to set your heart and mind?

    ☐ Romans 8:5-6

    ☐ Colossians 3:1-3

What will you experience as a result?

You can assess where you are in your walk with the Lord by looking at the fruit of your life. If you are yielding to the tug of your unsurrendered soul and setting your mind on satisfying its cravings, it will be evident. But if you are daily—choice-by-choice walking according to the Spirit, that will be evident as well.

Read Galatians 5:19-21 below and circle which fruit of the sinful nature you struggle with most often.

"Now the works of the flesh are evident, which are: adultery, fornication, uncleanness, lewdness, idolatry, sorcery, hatred, contentions, jealousies, outbursts of wrath, selfish ambitions, dissensions, heresies, envy, murders, drunkenness, revelries, and the like; of which I tell you beforehand, just as I also told you in time past, that those who practice such things will not inherit the kingdom of God."

Pray and repent; asking for forgiveness of your sin in this area. Ask the Lord to help you be watchful and vigilant in the Spirit and to choose not to yield to the pull of your soul or the enemy in this area, but instead to submit to and obey the Holy Spirit working in you!

Read Galatians 5:22-23 below and circle which fruits of the Spirit are most evident in your life.

"But the fruit of the Spirit is love, joy, peace, longsuffering, kindness, goodness, faithfulness, gentleness, self-control. Against such there is no law."

Thank the Lord for the leading of His Spirit and the resulting fruit in your life! Remember, God is not finished with you—He will keep working!

How do you walk in the Spirit?

You walk in the Spirit daily, *circumspectly* (watchful and vigilant), *step-by-step, listening* for His voice, with *purpose* and *thanksgiving*, choosing to follow the leading of the Holy Spirit instead of the desires of your flesh.

Romans 15:4 tells us, "For whatever things were written before were written for our learning, that we through patience and comfort of the Scriptures might have hope."

Just as words of testimony were written down—words of failure were also recorded. Both teach those who are willing to learn. Let's apply this Biblical principle of learning from the past and gain hope by journaling about the following areas.

Record a time when you walked in the Spirit. _____

_____

_____

_____

_____

_____

_____

What happened? _____

_____

_____

Praise the Lord for the victory—for it is God working in you to give you the desire and power to obey Him (Philippians 2:13, NLT)!

Record a time when you did not walk in the Spirit. _____

_____

_____

_____

_____

_____

What were the results? _____

_____

_____

_____

What would you do differently? _____

_____

_____

_____

Ask the Lord to help you in the future—remember, it is God working in you to give you the desire and power to obey Him (Philippians 2:13, NLT)!

Prayer

Commitment

What is your prayer regarding what you have learned and how you desire to put it into practice? Write it here. This is a safe place to pour out your heart before the Lord. It is your chance...

    ... to ask for His strength and guidance and know He will give it!

    ... to express your fears and know He will help you overcome them!

    ... to make a commitment to walk in the Spirit and know He will give you the desire and the power to do so! _____

_____

_____

_____

_____

_____

_____

_____

Let this be a reminder of your commitment to the Lord and His covenant with you!

Signature _____ Date _____

John Bevere
More Than 400,000 Copies in Print

THE
BAIT
OF
SATAN

Living Free
From the Deadly
Trap of Offense

10th Anniversary Edition
DEVOTIONAL SUPPLEMENT INCLUDED

Chapters 1-7 Notes: _____

_____

_____

_____

_____

_____

_____

_____

_____

_____

_____

_____

_____

To Summarize:

Which truth had the greatest impact on you? _____

_____

_____

_____

What was the most practical thing you learned? _____

_____

_____

_____

How are you going to apply what you learned? _____

_____

_____

_____

Session Two:

Commit
Everything to God

Trust in the Lord with all your heart,
and lean not on your own understanding;
in all your ways acknowledge Him,
and He will direct your paths.

Proverbs 3:5-6 (NKJ)

Session Two:
Commit Everything to God

Complete the following
homework assignments:

- □ **Workbook Section**
  Commit Everything to God

- □ **Book** Chapters 8-Epilogue
  The Bait of Satan
  by Dr. John Bevere

Continue the previous
discipleship assignments:

- □ **Daily personal devotional**
  ...Prayer
  ...Bible Reading (see reverse)

Add the following
discipleship assignments:

- □ **Prayer partnership** with a
  prayer partner or if married
  with spouse

- □ **Regular attendance** in your
  local congregation and at
  the Cleansing Stream
  Seminar Group

Session Two:
Commit Everything to God

*Trust in the Lord with all your heart, and lean not
on your own understanding; in all your ways
acknowledge Him, and He will direct your paths.*
Proverbs 3:5-6

Devotional Bible Reading

Week One

□ Day 1:	John 15	Psalm 15
□ Day 2:	John 16	Psalm 16
□ Day 3:	John 17	Psalm 17
□ Day 4:	John 18	Psalm 18
□ Day 5:	John 19	Psalm 19
□ Day 6:	John 20	Psalm 20
□ Day 7:	John 21	Psalm 21

Week Two

□ Day 1:	Romans 1	Psalm 22
□ Day 2:	Romans 2	Psalm 23
□ Day 3:	Romans 3	Psalm 24
□ Day 4:	Romans 4	Psalm 25
□ Day 5:	Romans 5	Psalm 26
□ Day 6:	Romans 6	Psalm 27
□ Day 7:	Romans 7	Psalm 28

Prayer
Partnership

Today the call is to *Commit Everything to God.* He is trustworthy! But He calls you beyond just relationship with Him... into relationship with others. This session you will be implementing prayer partnership and regular attendance in your local congregation and at the Cleansing Stream Seminar Group.

Why Pray with others?

- ☐ 1 Peter 4:8-10 points you to others, *And above all things have fervent love for* **one another,** *for 'love will cover a multitude of sins.' Be hospitable to* **one another** *without grumbling. As each one has received a gift, minister it to* **one another,** *as good stewards of the manifold grace of God.*

- ☐ James 5:16 directs us to be transparent in your prayer with others, *Confess your trespasses to* **one another,** *and pray for* **one another...**

How do you implement it?

- ☐ Do it regularly – it just takes a few minutes!
- ☐ Express your needs – be transparent and listen to their needs
- ☐ Pray for one another together
- ☐ Mutually encourage one another

There is a promise – if you do what Matthew 18:19 says, *...if two or three of you agree concerning anything they ask,* **it will be done** *for them by My Father in heaven.* God will answer!

About the Discipleship Assignment

Regular

Attendance

Why Meet with Others?

- ☐ Hebrews 10:24-25 calls you to, *…consider **one another** in order to stir up love and good works, not forsaking the assembling of **ourselves together**, as is the manner of some, but exhorting **one another**, and so much the more as you see the Day approaching.*

How do you implement it?

- ☐ It is not based on feelings, but choice!

- ☐ By committing to regularly attend church services.

- ☐ By committing to regularly attend your Cleansing Stream Seminar group and to be committed, involved and accountable.

As you partner with others in prayer and meeting together you will find encouragement on your way.

What does it mean to *Commit* Everything to God?

Scriptures

Then Elijah stood in front of them and said, "How long are you going to waver between two opinions? If the Lord is God, follow Him! But if Baal is God, then follow him!" But the people were completely silent.
1 Kings 18:21 (NLT)

Trust in the Lord with all your heart, and lean not on your own understanding; in all your ways acknowledge Him, and He shall direct your paths.
Proverbs 3:5-6

And you shall love the Lord your God with all your heart, with all your soul, with all your mind, and with all your strength. Mark 12:30

Theme Scripture:

Trust in the Lord with all your heart, and lean not on your own understanding; in all your ways acknowledge Him, and He shall direct your paths.
Proverbs 3:5-6

Definition:

"Commit"
    To pledge to do something, to make a binding declaration, to be bound, to trust

Quotes

"Commitment is more than a contribution (remember the pig and the chicken)!"

What does it mean to *Commit* Everything to God?

Things... Others... Yourself

Scriptures

Then God instructed the people as follows: "I am the Lord your God, who rescued you from slavery in Egypt. Do not worship any other gods besides me. Do not make idols of any kind..."
Exodus 20:1-4 (NLT)

(Look at the birds)
Matthew 6:26-30 (NLT)

(Seek ye first) Matthew 6:33

If you want to be My follower you must love Me more than your own father and mother, wife and children, brothers and sisters—yes, more than your own life. Otherwise, you cannot be My disciple. And you cannot be My disciple if you do not carry your own cross and follow Me.
Luke 14:26-27 (NLT)

Search me, O God, and know my heart; test me and know my thoughts. Point out anything in me that offends you and lead me along the path of everlasting life.
Psalm 139:23-24 (NLT)

I myself no longer live, but Christ lives in me. So I live my life in this earthly body by trusting in the Son of God, who loved me and gave Himself for me.
Galatians 2:20 (NLT)

Quotes

"Where am I spending my time? Where am I spending my money? What are the things that preoccupy my thoughts? What are the habits and patterns that I have gotten into that exclude God, the purpose of God, God's call, God's direction, my love for God?"

What does it mean to commit everything to God?

Commitment involves trusting—*trusting* the One who has proven Himself to be trustworthy. And placing in His hands anything that would distract, be an obstacle, or be used to assault your soul on your path as you walk in the Spirit. Everything you are and everything you have belong to Him anyway—you are just putting them back in their rightful place and adjusting your perspective!

Why *Commit* Everything to God?

Scriptures

We demolish arguments and every pretension that sets itself up against the knowledge of God, and we take captive every thought to make it obedient to Christ. 2 Corinthians 10:4-5 (NIV)

Take My yoke upon you and learn from Me, for I am gentle and lowly in heart, and you will find rest for your souls. Matthew 11:29

(Disciples in the storm) Mark 4:35-41

Rest... Faith... Release

Quotes

"Trusting Him is not an event—it is a lifestyle."

"The more we learn to overcome our fears in not trusting the more we learn to rest."

"Choose first to believe God and His Word. Start capturing your thoughts with the truth. Be led by God's promises not your feelings. Combat your fears by trusting God."

Why commit everything to God?

When you turn it all over to Him you will keep *growing*, experience *rest*, and *shine* His light to those around you.

How do you *Commit* Everything to God?

Trust God... Not my Understanding

"If I keep it (what I should commit to God) in my hands I get what I can do—my ability, my talent, my effort, my energy, my strength, and my reasoning."

"If I put this in others hands I get what others can do—their gifting and abilities may be different from mine but it is still going to be limited to the best they can do."

"If I hold on to it I get what I can do. If I give it to others I get what they can do. But if I give it to God I get what God can do."

How do you *Commit* Everything to God?

Scriptures

Trust in the Lord with all your heart, and lean not on your own understanding; in all your ways acknowledge Him, and He shall direct your paths.
Proverbs 3:5-6

Thus says the Lord: "Let not the wise man glory in his wisdom, let not the mighty man glory in his might, nor let the rich man glory in his riches." Jeremiah 9:23

The Test—Distractions... Obstacles... Assaults

Quotes

"The Test:

Test#1—What **distracts** you from your walk in the Spirit?

Test#2—What is an **obstacle** that keeps you from moving forward on your walk in the Spirit?

Test#3—What areas are being used by the enemy to **assault** you and keep you from walking in the Spirit?

These areas need to be committed to the Lord!"

How do you *Commit* Everything to God?

Scriptures

Give all your worries and cares to God, for He cares about what happens to you.
1 Peter 5:7 (NLT)

(Built up in our faith)
Jude 20

The Process—
Revelation... Repentance... Release
—With Thanksgiving!

Quotes

"*Revelation*—Ask the Lord to show you where to start.

Repentance—Repent for those things you've made an idol or put as priorities before God.

Release—Begin to exercise faith and trust God in those areas and make a choice to release them to His care."

"Commit daily, moment-by-moment and practice thankfulness."

"He not only cares for you He also knows how to care for you."

How do you commit everything to God?

Daily include the principle of **Revelation**—seeking the Lord for what distractions, obstacles and assaults are against your walk. Then following up with **Repentance** and **Release**. Begin by choosing to *trust* Him. Let yourself *lean* upon His ways as they are revealed to you in His Word. *Acknowledge* Him by bringing your life—everything you face—before Him, and allow Him to direct your walk on His path to fulfill His perfect plan. And be thankful—it is an ongoing process!

In Summary:

What does it mean to commit everything to God?

Commitment involves trusting—*trusting* the One who has proven Himself to be trustworthy. And placing in His hands anything that would distract, be an obstacle, or be used to assault your soul on your path as you walk in the Spirit. Everything you are and everything you have belong to Him anyway—you are just putting them back in their rightful place and adjusting your perspective!

Why commit everything to God?

When you turn it all over to Him you will keep *growing,* experience *rest,* and *shine* His light to those around you.

How do you commit everything to God?

Daily include the principle of **Revelation**—seeking the Lord for what distractions, obstacles and assaults are against your walk. Then following up with **Repentance** and **Release.** Begin by choosing to *trust* Him. Let yourself *lean* upon His ways as they are revealed to you in His Word. *Acknowledge* Him by bringing your life—everything you face—before Him, and allow Him to direct your walk on His path to fulfill His perfect plan. And be thankful—it is an ongoing process!

An Invitation...

We invite you to join us at a Regional Retreat! Register to attend with your group today!

Further Study

What does it mean to
Commit Everything to God?

Introduction

Freedom comes from knowing the truth, and that truth is found in the Word of God. The Bible contains everything you need to grow in your walk with the Lord. And as you walk in the Spirit, staying in step with His plans and purposes by submitting to His guidance, you can enjoy close friendship with God.

This submission is an integral part of being a true disciple of Jesus. Every day your choice to follow Him will be tested—both in big and small ways. The question is: What will you do? Will you maintain a strong commitment to the Lord or will you let yourself slowly slip into compromise?

The purpose of this session is to help you better understand how committed God is to you, and in doing so find the strength and peace you need to commit everything you are and have to Him.

In this session we will be answering three main questions.

□ *What* does it mean to commit everything to God?

□ *Why* commit everything to God?

□ *How* do you commit everything to God?

The key scripture for this study is Proverbs 3:5-6. Write it out below and then dive in. God's peace and grace be with you as you seek to know Him!

Proverbs 3:5-6

1.1 Commit Defined

Years ago there was a popular Christian song by gospel singer Bryan Duncan entitled "Have Yourself Committed." The song was a play on words about the need for believers to truly commit their lives to the Lord—just as fully and completely as if they were committing themselves into a hospital. Though the song was a humorous way of saying it, the truth is still clear: We need to be fully committed.

The word "commit" is defined as "to pledge to do something, to make a binding declaration, to trust." When you commit everything to God, you trust all that you are and all that concerns you into His care and keeping. Trusting is a choice you make. So, this is where the battle is fought. Will you bring your soul—your mind, emotions and will—under His authority and rest in the confidence that He will take care of everything? In other words, will you believe God or not?

Committing *everything* to God may seem difficult because too often those who were supposed to have kept their word didn't. This teaches distrust. But as you work through this Session, you will see how much God does care for you and how faithful He is to His Word.

Is it easy for you to trust God? Why or why not?

Read 1 Kings 18:21. Consider the question Elijah asked the people. If you had been among the people that day, what would your response have been?

As you work through this Session, God will reveal areas that are easy for you to commit and areas of struggle in your soul in which you need to grow in trust so you can commit more and more. God is going to work a miracle in your life over the next few weeks and teach you how to continue to trust Him—to commit everything to Him—like never before.

1.2 His Commitment to You and Your Commitment to Him

What do you think of when you see an engagement ring? Don't you automatically link a future wedding to whomever is wearing it? That ring is a quiet symbol with a loud message: "I'm going to be married!"

When you received God's gift of salvation, you received an engagement ring, too! It was not a shiny, gold band or glowing diamond—but something even *more* precious. The Bible says that God placed His Spirit in you as a deposit—an engagement ring, if you will—to tell everyone that you belong to Him and that one day He will come to take you home (see Ephesians 1:13-14). Now, that is commitment!

Read the following verses and briefly note what they say about God's commitment.

□ Numbers 23:19

□ 2 Timothy 2:13

How does knowing more about God's character help you to more fully trust Him?

More than merely a distant promise, God has made a real and honest commitment to you. He values you and longs to see you blessed and fulfilled, and He has extended all of Himself to make this possible. But what about you? What kind of commitment is God expecting from you, His child?

Read Mark 12:30. Notice the word "all" throughout this verse. In your own words, what does it mean to love God with all your heart, soul, mind, and strength?

Match the following.

Love God with all your heart   Your thoughts and reasonings

Love God with all your mind   Your physical efforts and abilities

Love God with all your soul   Your heart, mind, and will

Love God with all your strength   Your emotions and feelings

You must be willing to make more than a small contribution. Remember the example of bacon and eggs used in the teaching? The chicken made a *contribution* to the meal, but the pig made a *total commitment!* God does not just contribute—He is fully committed!

Like Him, you must be willing to wholeheartedly commit your life. This does not mean that you are enlisting in a program. Commitment is not about programs—it is about a Person. You commit to loving God. That is the key to ongoing spiritual growth.

1.3 What Keeps You from Committing?

As you have tried to walk in the Spirit, you have probably discovered areas of your soul that are difficult to commit to the Lord. Identifying what may be working against you helps you avoid traps and stay on the path.

These three sources—things, others, and even yourself—can be areas that distract, are obstacles, or can be used by the enemy to assault your soul and keep you from walking in the Spirit. As you look at each area ask yourself—*Is this a distraction to my walk? Is this an obstacle in my path? Is this an area where the enemy assaults me to keep me from walking in the Spirit?*

Things

People constantly strive for possessions—more stuff, better stuff, bigger stuff. In the quest to have everything, they can allow the desire for things to distract from their commitment to the Lord. Thankfully, Jesus gave the answer to this problem.

Read Matthew 6:25-31. What were some of the things Jesus said not to worry about?

Read Matthew 6:31-34. According to verse 32, why do you not have to worry about the things you need?

Instead of worrying about these things, what are you told to do (see verse 33)?

Others

In addition to possessions, relationships with others can become a hindrance to your walk with the Lord. While healthy relationships are vital to you, sometimes you can get stuck in unhealthy ones. What is the difference? In healthy relationships, you are encouraged to become all that God created you to be. These people hold you accountable for your choices and love you into wholeness. In unhealthy relationships, either you are controlled, manipulated, or forced into situations that squelch your ability to grow in the Lord, or you are controlling others. Sometimes your own need for acceptance or a fear of abandonment can drive you toward unhealthy relationships. Regardless of who or what, you must commit all your relationships to the Lord: family, friends and even enemies. By surrendering others to God, you give Him the opportunity to work His will in you and in them.

Who are the two closest people in your life? Describe a way each has impacted your life for good.

Luke 14:26-27 (NLT) tells us, "If you want to be My follower you must love Me more than your own father and mother, wife and children, brothers and sisters—yes, more than your own life. Otherwise, you cannot be My disciple. And you cannot be My disciple if you do not carry your own cross and follow Me."

What do you think Jesus meant by this bold statement?

Yourself

As if things and others weren't enough to keep you too preoccupied to lay your whole soul before the Lord—you also can be your own worst enemy! "Me?" you ask, "How?" It can happen by letting your weaknesses become excuses for not growing instead of reasons for coming to God for help.

It is easy to justify when you are not following through with what you know is right. That is why the psalmist David cried out, "Search me, O God, and know my heart" (see Psalm 139:23-24). He was asking God to take inventory of his soul—and to get rid of anything offensive (i.e. pride, anger, unforgiveness, etc.). Revelation is the key to seeing areas that need to be worked on (i.e. Are your hopes and dreams in line with His will? Is your time being spent as it should?, etc.) Sometimes this involves confession and repentance, sometimes recommitment and discipline, sometimes patience and endurance—and sometimes all of the above! Whatever the area of growth, God reveals the need and then provides the answer to it (see 2 Corinthians 12:9).

Make David's prayer, from Psalm 139, your own. Ask the Lord to reveal where you have hindered your own walk in the Spirit and have not trusted Him. Write down what He reveals.

Read Galatians 2:20. According to this verse, once you are saved, whose life are you living? How does this affect your attitudes and choices?

Proverbs 16:3 (Amplified) says, "Roll your works upon the Lord [commit and trust them wholly to Him; He will cause your thoughts to become agreeable to His will, and] so shall your plans be established and succeed."

What are you told to commit to the Lord?

What are the results if you do?

God does not want anything between you and Him. That's why anything that overshadows His place as Lord of your life needs to be brought back into its rightful place. Your heart belongs to Him; you belong to Him!

Look back over the three areas addressed in this section. Prayerfully identify one item in each category that hinders your walk with the Lord and write them in the following chart.

Commit Everything to God		
Things	Others	Me

What does it mean to commit everything to God?

Commitment involves *trusting*—trusting the One who has proven Himself to be trustworthy and placing in His hands anything that would distract, obstruct, or be used to assault your soul on your path. Everything you are and everything you have belong to Him anyway—you are just putting them back in their rightful place and adjusting your perspective!

Why *Commit* Everything to God?

2.1 Growth... Rest... Testimony
Committing Keeps You Growing

Committed lives are growing lives because they invite the presence of God to work in and through them to strengthen, mature and establish His plans and purposes. As difficult as it may be at times to truly release something to the Lord, every time you do, your will is strengthened and He works His perfect will in that area of your life.

As you may have noticed, committing everything to God is a continual choice to surrender to Him—and this is why walking in the Spirit is essential. It works two ways—you need to walk in the Spirit to identify areas that need to be committed and as you commit those areas, it is easier to walk in the Spirit! When you walk in the Spirit, you allow your choices and decisions to be directed by Him. In doing so, you are laying down your life and trusting Him to remove what could hinder your walk. Your mind and heart can hold back and want to "play it safe" so that you don't get hurt. But God wants you to step out and fully trust Him. Each time you do, it gets easier and easier because He continually proves Himself faithful!

Read 2 Corinthians 10:5. What does it say you are to do with your thoughts? (It works for feelings, too!)

Read Colossians 3:16. How would the Word dwelling in you help you take your thoughts (and feelings) captive, making them obedient to Christ?

The more you learn to commit everything to God, the more it becomes a lifestyle rather than an event. As you daily turn over your possessions, relationships, responsibilities and time to Him, you find His faithfulness leads you ever onward in peaceful trust. What will be the result of committing yourself to God and His Word? You will be built up! That means growth—and that's good!

Committing Gives You Rest

Another benefit of committing everything to God is that it brings your soul to a place of true rest. By releasing all you have and all you are to the Lord, you leave the present and the future in His hands. This is not a lazy resignation, but an active faith that believes in the power and goodness of God. Committing everything to God is like moving out of the driver's seat and allowing Him to take you where He wants you to go. You can rest in the confidence that He not only knows the way, but has the ability to get you there safely.

In Exodus 33:14 The Lord said, "My presence will go with you and I will give you rest."

Joshua 1:13 says, "Remember the word which Moses the servant of the Lord commanded you, saying, 'The Lord your God is giving you rest and is giving you this land.'"

Matthew 11:29 (Amplified) says, "Take My yoke upon you and learn of Me, for I am gentle (meek) and humble (lowly) in heart, and you will find rest (relief and ease and refreshment and recreation and blessed quiet) for your souls."

Underline what God promises you. Which of these verses is especially meaningful to you at this point in your life?

How do you enter this rest? By trusting God! Think about the deliverance of God's people from Egypt. They had committed to Him, and He brought them out of slavery with many powerful miracles. But even though they had walked through parted waters, they forgot God's power and love and began to draw back in unbelief and disobedience.

Read Hebrews 4:1-11. According to verses 2 and 6, why did the Israelites not enter God's rest?

Faith is the key to rest. By faith, you commit everything to God. You stop striving in your own strength to attain or achieve and allow the Lord to work by His Spirit in your life to accomplish His will. There may be times when it feels like you cannot trust God with something. Just like the Israelites, you may want to take back what you have committed to Him. This is not something to feel defeated by; rather, it is a point of growth. You can always come back to that place of committing it to Him. Sometimes this means committing the same thing over and over again to Him. That's okay. The point is you are doing it—you are repenting for taking it back and releasing it to Him again and believing that He will take care of it, so you will be able to leave it.

Committing Is a Testimony to Others of God's Faithfulness

Have you ever been around someone who exhibits true confidence and peace? Doesn't their state of mind influence you to a better way of living? It should. God wants your life to spill over into those around you, drawing them to a closer relationship with Him. When you are continually committing everything to the Lord, entering the place of rest that faith opens up to us, you can influence others to move closer to Him.

Who do you know that exhibits true confidence and peace? What is it about them that influenced your life for the better? Record your answers in the following chart.

Name	Influence on your life

Read Matthew 5:16. What does it mean to "let your light shine?"

What is the result of it?

List a way your life inspires those around you to trust in God.

As you continue to walk in the Spirit, committing everything to God, His power will enable you to shine your light! Through Him you can be an example of God's faithfulness, demonstrating that what He has done for you, He will do for anyone who will open their heart and commit everything to Him.

Why commit everything to God?

When you turn it all over to Him, you will keep *growing*, experience *rest*, and *shine* His light to those around you. What better reasons could you need?

How do you Commit Everything to God?

3.1 A Personal Choice

You began this session of the workbook with Proverbs 3:5-6. In the *New King James Version* of these verses you read the words "trust," "lean" and "acknowledge." These are three key points you must embrace in order to commit everything to God as you successfully walk in the Spirit.

Trust

> "Trust in the Lord with all your heart..." Proverbs 3:5

Create your own version of this verse.

To trust someone is to count them as honest, reliable and trustworthy. The foundation for being able to commit everything to God is your decision to trust Him and His heart toward you. The greater your trust, the greater His work in you. This is why you must trust Him with all your **heart** (defined as *who you are, your inner most being*) and *soul* (your *mind, emotions and will*). Remember, from Session One, your soul is in the process of sanctification— learning to surrender and submit. As you learned earlier, you cannot merely contribute a portion to God, you must release it all if you want to grow in your walk with Him and experience His peace and rest. Did you trust Him with your eternal salvation? Then trust Him with your present and future here on earth! Trust Him with your every need. Trust Him with your family and friends. Trust Him with your hopes and dreams.

Jesus Himself spoke of the great things that will happen as you choose to have faith in God. Read Mark 11:22-24. Trust is a choice on your part to believe that God is honest and reliable. According to verse 24 what two things are we to do?

Lean

"...and lean not on your own understanding..." Proverbs 3:5

What does this mean to you? Write it in your own words.

Have you ever played the game where you fall back with your eyes closed and let someone you trust catch you from behind? Once you have made the decision to believe that God is trustworthy, then you can fall back into His arms with joy and confidence. This is a perfect picture of what it means to lean on Him. When you commit everything to God, you cease to lean on your own understanding and instead lean on His, allowing His Word and wisdom to guide your life.

Sometimes God's ways do not reconcile with your human reasoning, but if you are to live committed to Him, then you must keep leaning on His Word and wisdom—no matter what! Don't be surprised if that leaning brings you to unexpected places!

Match the following scriptures with God's wisdom.

Proverbs 15:1	God's wisdom says to love your enemies.
Matthew 5:43-44	God's wisdom says gentleness conquers anger.
Matthew 10:39	God's wisdom says weakness is strength.
2 Corinthians 12:10	God's wisdom says lose your life and you find it.

All of these ideas are contrary to the conventional way of thinking, but if you take God at His Word and lean on it, you will see His plans accomplished in you. God's wisdom says to trust when you can't see and believe when you don't understand. This is leaning on His understanding instead of yours.

Acknowledge

"In all your ways acknowledge Him, and He shall direct your paths."

Proverbs 3:6

Circle the action required on our part and underline the promised provision on God's part.

You choose to *trust*. You let yourself *lean*. The point of actual committing is when you *acknowledge* the Lord. To acknowledge God in all your ways means that you bring everything before Him, asking that He govern every part of your life in accordance with His plan and purpose.

It means that you go to Him first, trusting Him and leaning on His wisdom rather than making your own plans and later asking for His blessing. Can you see how this relates to walking in the Spirit? In order to commit everything to God, you must continually rely upon the power and the direction of the Holy Spirit and surrender your soul to His leading.

As you worked through this section, you may have identified areas needing to be committed. List them in the following chart. Ask yourself, "Where do I need to trust? Where do I need to lean? Where do I need to acknowledge Him?"

Commit Everything to God		
"Trust"	"Lean"	"Acknowledge"

3.2 The Test!

Working through this Session, you have begun to identify areas of your soul that are in the sanctification process and still need to be committed to God! As you continue with this section, look for God to reveal unsurrendered thoughts or feelings and to identify choices and actions that are not Spirit-led.

Distractions

Test#1—What distracts you from your walk in the Spirit?

Worry can be a distraction that can drive you off course without you even knowing it. There are some distractions that may seem valid and worth listening to, but worry is just unbelief in disguise. Worry is choosing not to trust Him. Other distractions include unhealthy relationships, an unguarded drive to earn money, or self-ambition to succeed. Committing everything to God means you are choosing to trust Him with whatever distracts you.

Try Test #1 and write what you identified in the chart at the end of this section.

Obstacles

Test#2—What is an obstacle that keeps you from moving forward in your walk in the Spirit?

Along with distractions, you may come upon an outright roadblock in your walk with the Lord. Roadblocks are more obvious than distractions and may be very difficult to remove, such as persecution or unforgiveness. Only the wisdom and grace of God can direct us around, over, or through an obstacle. This is why you must continually be ready, all of the time, to receive His instructions. Through the power of God, every obstacle can be dealt with and you will walk on in peace!

Try Test #2 and write what you identified in the chart at the end of this section.

Assaults

Test#3—What areas are being used by the enemy to assault you and keep you from walking in the Spirit?

Distractions and obstacles are often just the results of living in a broken world. Beyond them, the devil may come to attack our faith in God and try to uproot His Word planted in you. Though the devil's power has been broken, he still roams the earth looking to bring as much destruction as he can. You have the armor of God and the authority of Jesus to stand against the devil and see the doors of your life shut to his attacks.

Try Test #3.

What distractions, obstacles and areas of assault need to be committed to the Lord? Write what you identified in the chart.

Commit Everything to God		
Distractions	Obstacles	Assaults

In **Proverbs 4:11-15 (NIV)** God says, "I guide you in the way of wisdom and lead you along straight paths (avoiding distractions). When you walk, your steps will not be hampered; when you run, you will not stumble (overcoming obstacles). Hold on to instruction, do not let it go; guard it well, for it is your life. Do not set foot on the path of the wicked or walk in the way of evil men. Avoid it, do not travel on it; turn from it and go on your way (conquering the enemy)."

*Accept His help and make this your prayer for **distractions**... "Lord guide me in the way of wisdom and lead me along straight paths instead of the way of distraction."*

*Make this your prayer for **obstacles**... "Lord guide me in my walk so my steps will not be hampered; when I run, I will not stumble or be tripped up by obstacles."*

*Make this your prayer for **assaults**... "Help me to hold on to instruction and not let go; to guard it, for it is my life. Help me not to set my foot on the path of the wicked or walk in the way of evil. Help me to avoid it, do not travel on it; turn from it and conquer the enemy's assaults."*

3.3 The Process—Revelation, Repentance, Release

Now that you have identified areas that need to be committed, you can begin the process of committing and releasing them to the Lord.

Step #1: Revelation

Read the following scriptures and circle the sources of revelation that can help you understand areas of sin in your life.

John 8:32 says, "You shall know the truth, and the truth shall make you free."

John 14:26 (Amplified) tells us that "...the Comforter (Counselor, Helper, Intercessor, Advocate, Strengthener, Standby), the Holy Spirit, Whom the Father will send in My name [in My place, to represent Me and act on My behalf], He will teach you all things. And He will cause you to recall (will remind you of, bring to your remembrance) everything I have told you."

The Word and Holy Spirit are keys to seeing areas needing to be committed. Ask the Lord to show you areas that you are holding on to: where you are not trusting, where you are leaning on your own understanding, where you are not acknowledging Him and areas being used to distract, as an obstacle or provide a place for the enemy to assault you.

Are there any other areas the Lord has revealed (in addition to the places mentioned previously)? As God reveals any other areas, write them down here and thank Him for the revelation because it is a step on the path of committing everything to Him.

Step #2: Repentance

What does 2 Corinthians 7:10 say about repentance?

Repentance is taking what has been revealed, being convicted of your sin and with sorrow telling the Lord you are sorry for not trusting Him—for holding back. It is telling Him your desire—to be able to choose to commit all areas to Him. It is the time to declare your choice for Him to be the one and only Lord of your life in each area revealed.

Step #3: Release

Psalm 37:5 says, "Commit everything you do to the Lord. Trust him, and He will help you."

Circle the two things you are to do. Underline what you are assured God will do.

First, release any unforgiveness or past hurts that have made you hesitant to trust God. Ask the Holy Spirit to come along side of you and bring those places of brokenness to wholeness. Then, begin to exercise faith and trust in God as you commit and release these areas to Him. Release means to purposely make a choice to give each area to the Lord and His care.

This process can become a habit during your daily, personal devotional prayer time. Then, by sharing what God has revealed to you with someone who can hold you accountable for your decision—perhaps your prayer partner or your small group—you will continue to grow in your walk with the Lord. (Incorporating prayer partnership and regular attendance at your Cleansing Stream Group and Church are your Discipleship Assignments this session. These are good places to receive encouragement and support as you learn to commit!)

Here's a sample prayer for the process.

Father, I know You want what is best for me.
Revelation: Thank You for revealing areas in my life that are not fully committed to You.

Repentance: I repent for not trusting You in these areas. I do not want anything to come before You or to be between us.

Release: I lay down all I have, my relationships, my desires and ambitions, my choices and plans, before You now and commit them into Your hands. I release these specific areas (list them) to you and choose to trust You. In Jesus' name. Amen.

Take a moment right now and go through the process outlined previously. Prayerfully choose three areas identified through **revelation** from God that need to be committed to Him.

See the charts or notes you wrote under the following sections:
1.3 "What Keeps You from Committing,"
3.1 "A Personal Choice,"
3.2 "The Test"
3.3 "The Process—Step #1 Revelation"

Area #1:

Area #2:

Area #3:

One by one, **repent** of not trusting the Lord in each area.

Now **release** each one to His care. Afterward, rejoice before the Lord! Thank Him for His faithfulness!

3.4 The Ongoing Process of Commitment with Thanksgiving!

By now you may be thinking maybe it might not be that hard to commit. Actually, committing an area to the Lord may not be as easy as you think, but holding on to that place of surrender and leaving it in the Lord's hands might be even more difficult. Keeping everything committed to God means that you make an ongoing choice to trust Him.

While you walk on this earth, you will face many things that will challenge your trust and commitment of these areas to the Lord. If you allow things like fear or unforgiveness to take root in your heart, then you will miss the blessing God wants to pour into your life.

What can you do? Are you relegated to a life of wavering back and forth between committing and taking back? No! It's an ongoing process that requires time and patience. Instead of longing for the day when you will never have to struggle again, learn to enjoy the process and the power and presence of the Lord at work in you as you face challenges.

Part of learning to enjoy the process is to begin practicing thankfulness.

Psalm 69:30 (NIV) says, "I will praise God's name in song and glorify Him with thanksgiving."

Circle what the psalmist chose to do.

Think about all God has already done to bring freedom and deliverance to you. By offering praise to Him, you are acknowledging that He is able to meet all of your needs.

Take a minute to praise and thank God for what He has revealed and His promises to walk you through each point of commitment. Summarize your praise and thanksgiving (think of it as your first psalm)!

Do you remember the illustration from the teaching about growing in faith? As a child, you learn in little ways to depend upon the Lord. These "little victories" build your faith and enable you to trust the Lord with more difficult situations, as you get older. The point is the process. You commit everything to God daily—sometimes even moment-by-moment. Things will get easier as you, choice-by-choice, commit everything to the Lord.

Sometimes you will commit a specific area to the Lord then take it back by falling into worry and concern over it. Do not be discouraged. There is no penalty for coming back to the Lord; in fact, it is a *good* sign! Realizing that you need to commit something again to the Lord shows that you are walking in the Spirit and listening to His prompting. The Bible is clear that God never condemns you for needing His help. He willingly and freely extends His grace to you if you come to Him in repentance and in faith.

A Word of Encouragement

Committing everything to the Lord is an ongoing process, so enjoy the journey! Keep yourself surrendered in faith to God. As you do, you will grow stronger and stronger in the Lord and sharpen your ability to walk in the Spirit as you commit everything to God.

Read 1 Peter 5:7 (NIV), placing your name at the beginning of the scripture. _____, "cast all your anxiety (care) on Him because He cares for you."

What are you called to do? (Note this is an area of trust and commitment.)

Why can you cast all your anxiety and care upon the Lord?

How do you commit everything to God?

Daily ask for **Revelation**—seeking the Lord for what distractions, obstacles and assaults are against your walk. Then follow up with **Repentance** and **Release**. Begin by choosing to *trust* Him. Let yourself *lean* upon His ways as they are revealed to you in His Word. *Acknowledge* Him by bringing your life—before Him, and allow Him to direct your walk on His path to fulfill His perfect plan, which is tailor-made for you. And be thankful—it is an ongoing process!

Romans 15:4 tells us, "For whatever things were written before were written for our learning, that we through patience and comfort of the Scriptures might have hope."

Just as words of testimony were written down—words of failure were also recorded. Both teach those who are willing to learn. Let's apply this Biblical principle of learning from the past and gain hope by journaling about the following areas.

Record a specific time when you did commit an area of your life to the Lord and left it with Him.

_____

_____

_____

_____

_____

_____

_____

_____

How did it impact your life? _____

_____

_____

_____

Praise the Lord for the victory—thank Him for helping you to trust Him—He did give you the desire and power to obey Him (Philippians 2:13, NLT)!

Record a time you did not choose to commit an area to the Lord. _____

_____

_____

_____

_____

How did it impact your walk?_____

_____

_____

_____

What would you do differently now?_____

_____

_____

_____

Ask the Lord to help you at each point of commitment—remember, it is Him working in you to give you the desire and power to commit everything (Philippians 2:13, NLT)!

Prayer

Commitment

What is your prayer regarding what you have learned and how you desire to put it into practice? Write it here. This is a safe place to pour out your heart before the Lord. It is your chance...
...to ask for His strength and guidance and know He will give it!
...to express your fears and know He will help you overcome them!
...to commit everything to God and know He will help you, choice-by-choice!

_____

_____

_____

_____

_____

_____

_____

_____

_____

Let this be a reminder of your commitment to the Lord and His covenant with you!

Signature _____ Date _____

During the Homework

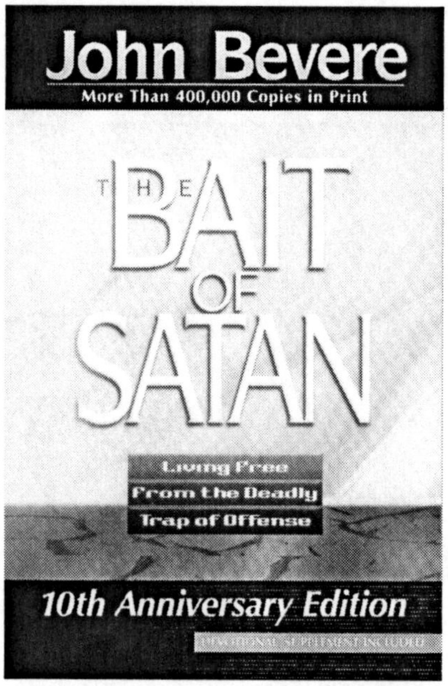

John Bevere
More Than 400,000 Copies in Print
THE BAIT OF SATAN
Living Free From the Deadly Trap of Offense
10th Anniversary Edition

Chapters 8-Epilogue Notes: ______

To Summarize:

Which truth had the greatest impact on you? ______

What was the most practical thing you learned? ______

How are you going to apply what you learned? ______

Session Three:
Speak Words of Life

*Death and life are
in the power of the tongue.*
Proverbs 18:21 (NKJ)

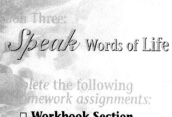

Session Three:

Speak Words of Life

plete the following
mework assignments:

- ☐ **Workbook Section**
  Speak Words of Life
- ☐ **Audio** teaching of
  *Building a House of Worship
  Where You Live*
  by Dr. Jack Hayford
- ☐ **Book**
  Winning Spiritual Warfare
  by Neil Anderson

the previous
cipleship assignments:

- ☐ **Daily personal devotional**
  ...Prayer
  ...Bible Reading (see reverse)
- ☐ **Prayer partnership** with a
  prayer partner or if married
  with spouse
- ☐ **Regular attendance** in your
  local congregation and at
  the Cleansing Stream
  Seminar Group

the following
discipleship assignments:

- ☐ **Worship** by singing a song
  during your *devotional* and
  before a *meal*
- ☐ **Bible Reading out loud:**
  Couples: Husband reads the
  second chapter to wife
  Individuals: read second
  chapter out loud

© Copyright 2003 Cleansing Stream Ministries

Session Three:

Speak Words of Life

Death and life are in the power of the tongue.
Proverbs 18:21

Devotional Bible Reading

Week One

		Devotional	Out Loud
☐	Day 1:	Romans 8	Psalm 29
☐	Day 2:	Romans 9	Psalm 30
☐	Day 3:	Romans 10	Psalm 31
☐	Day 4:	Romans 11	Psalm 32
☐	Day 5:	Romans 12	Psalm 33
☐	Day 6:	Romans 13	Psalm 34
☐	Day 7:	Romans 14	Psalm 35

Week Two

		Devotional	Out Loud
☐	Day 1:	Romans 15	Psalm 36
☐	Day 2:	Romans 16	Psalm 37
☐	Day 3:	James 1	Psalm 38
☐	Day 4:	James 2	Psalm 39
☐	Day 5:	James 3	Psalm 40
☐	Day 6:	James 4	Psalm 41
☐	Day 7:	James 5	Psalm 42

Worship

Today the Lord is calling you to *Speak Words of Life*—planting good seed into your own soil (your soul) and into that of others. The disciplines you are implementing provide several great ways to do just that!

Why worship ...in your personal devotional time?
    ...with your family?

- ☐ Psalm 100:4 calls you to, *Enter into His gates with thanksgiving, and into His courts with praise.*
    - ▪ You enter into **His presence** through praise and worship!
- ☐ Psalm 22:3 tells you the result, *But You are holy, enthroned in the praises of Israel.*
    - ▪ He enters into **our present situation** through praise and worship!
- ☐ You enter His presence and invite Him to enter your present circumstances!

How do you implement it?

- ☐ Do it daily!
    - ▪ Try one song with your personal devotional time
    - ▪ Incorporate another worship song at a meal
- ☐ Choose a familiar one and sing it several times
- ☐ As you sing, reflect on the Lord and the attributes that are being expressed
- ☐ As you do—you will enter His presence and He will enter your present circumstances!

About the Discipleship Assignment

Out Loud

Bible Reading

Why read the Word out loud?

- ☐ Deuteronomy 6:6-7 says, *And these words which I have commanded you today shall be in your heart. You shall teach them diligently to your children, and shall **talk of them** when you **sit** in your house, when you **walk** by the way, when you **lie down** and when you **rise up.***

- ☐ You have spoken many other words in your home; why not invite the life in the Word of God?

How do you implement it?

- ☐ Choose to press past the thoughts and feelings that would say this is weird.

- ☐ Begin by standing in the center of the living room and reading out loud the chapter assigned for that day.

- ☐ Initially you may want to read out loud in a different room each day until you have established the Word throughout your house!

- ☐ Continue to read the Word out loud daily. Deuteronomy gives us options of how to do it—sitting, walking, laying down and getting up!

Daily incorporating worship into your personal devotional time and at a meal, as well as reading the Word of God out loud will plant good seed in your home... which will reproduce... bearing good fruit!

During the Teaching

What does it mean to *Speak* Words of Life?

Theme Scripture:

Death and life are in the power of the tongue, and those who love it will eat its fruit. Proverbs 18:21

Definition:

"Speak" to express

What does it mean to *Speak* Words of Life?

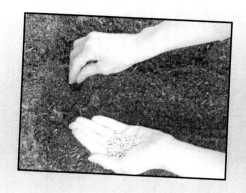

Scriptures

(God made us from dust)
Genesis 2:7

Receiving... Retaining... Reproducing

Quotes

"Your soul is what you know and understand and how you feel about what you know and understand."

"We can't cast out flesh, we need to get it submitted and crucified."

"We don't have to receive every word spoken. We don't have to retain every word we receive. But if we *receive* and if we *retain* we will *reproduce*."

What does it mean to speak words of life?

Words are like **seeds** that when spoken are sown into your soul or others'. You have a choice—you do not have to receive every word, you do not have to retain every word received, BUT if you *receive* and if you *retain*, the words will *reproduce*.

Why *Speak* Words of Life?

Scriptures

Let each of us please his neighbor for his good, leading to edification.
Romans 15:2

Now David was greatly distressed, for the people spoke of stoning him, because the soul of all the people was grieved, every man for his sons and his daughters. But David strengthened himself in the LORD his God. 1 Samuel 30:6

Quotes

Encourage—Others and Ourselves

Why *Speak* Words of Life?

Far Reaching... Long Lasting

Scriptures

A word fitly spoken is like apples of gold in settings of silver. Proverbs 25:11

Death and life are in the power of the tongue, and those who love it will eat its fruit. Proverbs 18:21

Looking carefully lest anyone fall short of the grace of God; lest any root of bitterness springing up cause trouble, and by this many become defiled. Hebrews 12:15

But I say to you that for every idle word men may speak, they will give account of it in the day of judgment. Matthew 12:36

Quotes

"**Curse:** Something spoken or written against an individual or group of individuals that contradicts the will of God as revealed in His Word."

"**Blessing:** A word or statement toward an individual or group of individuals, that is in full agreement with God's word and intended purpose."

"The effects of our words are far reaching and long lasting!"

"Remember: The *Right Seed* – The *Right Place* – The *Right Time!*"

Why speak words of life?

Good words *encourage* and build up those who hear them. Choosing your words carefully is important since their effects can be *far reaching* and *long lasting*. The right word at the right time can be a great blessing!

How do you *Speak* Words of Life?

Know the Lord... Avoid Judgments

Quotes

"We avoid so many problems when we don't fill in that blank 'why' and we go to the person instead."

How do you *Speak* Words of Life?

Test Words... Choose to Bless

Scriptures

Having wiped out the handwriting of requirements that was against us, which was contrary to us. And He has taken it out of the way, having nailed it to the cross.
Colossians 2:14

Quotes

"Test the words...
Are they from God? Do they agree with what He has already said in the Scriptures?

Are they from the flesh? Do they lead you to selfish actions and attitudes?

Are they from the devil? Do they slander or defame the Word of God or His character?"

"Just like we can't get the toothpaste back in the tube—what we speak, once it is out there can't be taken back. Sometimes the only thing to do is to *clean it up!*"

How do you speak words of life?

Know the Lord so that you can discern His voice. *Test the seed* to determine if it's from God. *Avoid judging* others; instead, bless them in word and deed. Do not grumble or complain against the work of God. But you do deal with the words—*repent, remove,* and *replace!*

In Summary:

What does it mean to speak words of life?

Words are like **seeds** that when spoken are sown into your soul or others'. You have a choice—you do not have to receive every word, you do not have to retain every word received, BUT if you *receive* and if you *retain*, the words will *reproduce*.

Why speak words of life?

Good words *encourage* and build up those who hear them. Choosing your words carefully is important since their effects can be *far reaching* and *long lasting*. The right word at the right time can be a great blessing!

How do you speak words of life?

Know the Lord so that you can discern His voice. *Test the seed* to determine if it's from God. *Avoid judging* others; instead, bless them in word and deed. Do not grumble or complain against the work of God. But you do deal with the words—*repent, remove,* and *replace!*

A Reminder...

Your attendance at the Regional Retreat is an integral part of the Seminar and should not be missed by anyone! Have you registered for the retreat?

Further Study

What does it mean to *Speak* Words of Life?

Introduction

Do you remember Session One? Good! See if you can complete this sentence: Walking in the Spirit means...

    A. ...that your feet never touch the ground.
    B. ...that you have arrived at perfect spiritual maturity.
    C. ...that you hum holiday tunes every day of the year.
    D. ...that you daily choose to be led by the Holy Spirit.

Hopefully you chose letter D as the correct answer (unless, of course, you are really into Christmas songs!). To walk in the Spirit means that you, day by day, step-by-step, choose to follow the leadership of the Holy Spirit rather than your own mind, will, or emotions. You continually surrender your choices and actions to Him, and allow Him to guide you. Next, you learned that you must commit everything to God, trusting Him with all you are and all you have. Like walking in the Spirit, committing everything to God is a daily decision to release our lives, possessions, relationships and futures to Him.

Now, let's learn more about speaking words of life by answering...

☐ *What* does it means to speak words of life?

☐ *Why* speak words of life?

☐ *How* do I speak words of life?

The key verse for this study is Proverbs 18:21. Write it out in the box below.

Proverbs 18:21

1.1 Sowing and Reaping Defined

Do you remember the last time you planted a seed? Were you surprised by what grew? Probably not. You knew that the seed you planted already determined what would be produced. Cherry seeds yield cherry trees. Apples seeds yield apple trees. Why? Because God made it that way. It is His law of sowing and reaping, and it applies to the natural world around us and to our spiritual lives as well.

Read the following verses and note what is being sown and reaped.

Bible Verse	Sown	Reaped
Proverbs 22:8a		
Hosea 10:12-13		
Galatians 6:8a		
Galatians 6:8b		

It's the way God has designed our world. We reap what we sow. The Parable of the Sower will help you begin to understand the power of words. In this Session we will focus on the seed being planted.

Mark 4:3 (NIV) says, "Listen! A farmer went out to sow his seed."

Circle what the farmer plants.

Mark 4:14 (NIV) "The farmer sows the word."

Underline what the seed is called in this verse.

The Word of God is often referred to as seed. When it is planted in our hearts, it grows and bears fruit that glorifies God. Just as planting an apple seed produces an apple tree, planting the incorruptible Word of God produces an incorruptible life.

Read the following verses and circle the effect the seed of God's Word has in you.

James 1:18 says, "Of His own will He brought us forth by the Word of truth, that we might be a kind of first fruits of His creatures."

1 Peter 1:23 says, "Having been born again, not of corruptible seed but incorruptible, through the Word of God which lives and abides forever."

When God's Word is planted in your soul (your mind and emotions), it takes root, grows and bears fruit. Then, you become a farmer who can likewise deposit the seed of God's Word in the lives of others. This is where things get tricky. All words act as seeds and are planted in the hearts of those listening—whether they are words that you speak to others or words that were spoken to you. During this Session, you will look at both *speaking* and *receiving* words.

1.2 Considering the Seed

God's Word is good seed that produces good fruit. Are there bad seeds, too? Unfortunately, there are. Many of the words that have been spoken over you, and even spoken by you, were not the good seed of God's Word, but the selfish, hurtful words of the flesh or the slandering, defeating words of the devil. Because of the law of sowing and reaping, the seed that is planted determines the harvest that will be produced. The natural process of *receiving, retaining* and *reproducing* can help you understand how spiritual seed gets planted in your heart.

Receiving

A seed must be received and nurtured before it will reproduce. As in the Parable of the Sower (you can read it again Mark 4:1-9, 13-20), some seed fell along the path and never even began to germinate or take root. That seed was not received into the soil. A seed that is not received cannot grow. Likewise, words that are spoken to you—whether by others or even in your own mind or heart—do not necessarily have to be received. Consider those words in light of the Word of God. You do not have to accept lies about yourself, your acceptance, or your future; you have the truth about these things from the Living Word of God!

Thinking back over the past few days, list one positive thing and one negative thing that have been spoken to you about your life, your future, or your destiny.

How do each of those words compare with what the Word of God says about you? (If you can, find a specific Bible verse to support your answer and write it here.)

Retaining

Once a seed has been accepted, it must remain in the ground to germinate and grow. In the Parable of the Sower, some seeds did make it into the ground, but they did not make it through the heat and were lost. When words are planted in your heart, you can retain them by believing them and meditating on them and cause them to grow. This nurtures the seed and allows it to root deeply in your soul. If the words you received and retained were good, then the harvest will be likewise good. But if the words were bad, then you are nurturing a destructive harvest.

A lot of your beliefs about yourself and the world come from the things you were told as a child. Children accept the words spoken to them much more eagerly than adults. Those early seeds can form vast root systems that either help you or hurt you as you grow up. The good news is that you can uproot a seed—even a whole plant!—and remove it by the power of the Holy Spirit.

List one or two words that were spoken to you as a child about yourself.

Reproducing

A seed that has been received and retained will automatically reproduce. The words that you have accepted and nurtured will likewise bring a harvest. This can be good news or bad news depending on the seed. As a Christian, though, it is important to remember that God's grace and mercy are available to cover all of your mistakes and heal all of your wounds. Nothing is too difficult for Him. His power is greater than anything.

The process of reproduction is the same whether you are speaking words to others or to yourself. Sometimes, you can be your own worst enemy. Whether spoken or thought, words of self-defeat and condemnation, when unchallenged, are able to send down deep roots.

You do not have to receive words that go against what the Bible has declared to be true about you. The Word of God and words that are consistent with it are the only seeds that need to remain in your life. You can refuse bad seeds and plant good ones in their place, seeds that will produce a harvest of righteousness and confidence in the Lord. Sow and grow orchards of love, joy, peace and patience!

What does it mean to speak words of life?

Words are like seeds that when spoken are sown into your life or others'. You have a choice—you do not have to receive every word, you do not have to retain every word received, BUT if you *receive* and if you *retain*, the words will *reproduce*.

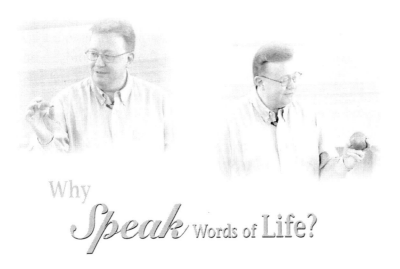

Why *Speak* Words of Life?

2.1 Encourage Others and Ourselves

Encouraging Others

As you have learned, speaking words of life involves both the words that
have been spoken to you and also those you speak to others. You have
looked at how words may have influenced your own life, but for a
moment, consider the words that you have spoken to others. Just like the
farmer in the Parable of the Sower, you, as a living epistle (see 2
Corinthians 3:2-3), have the ability to plant seeds in those around you.
So, what kind of seed will you plant?

Read Matthew 12:36. What words will you have to give an account for?

Read Ephesians 4:29; 5:4 and fill in the chart that follows.

Words not to speak...	Words to speak...

Though it is easy to allow yourself to speak whatever seems funny or
amusing at the moment, the Bible says foolish talking and inappropriate
joking are wrong. Why? Because they are seeds that will not produce a
wholesome harvest. This does not mean you can never joke around, but it
does mean that you should consider your words before you speak them.

Other words you should not speak are words of gossip, slander, criticism, lying, arguing, exaggerating, profanity, complaining and backbiting. These verses from Ephesians make it clear that your words should always build others up and benefit them. Every word you speak is a seed, and every seed has the power to reproduce. Plant seeds of hope and encouragement in the lives of others, not seeds of despair and defeat.

You know the words you speak are good seed—words of blessings—if they are in full agreement with God's Word and intended purpose. Anything less than that should remain unspoken. You want to speak words that line up with His Word. This means, of course, that you must know His Word! Spending time reading and studying the Bible will allow the Lord to plant lots of good seed in you. Then you will be able to plant that seed in the lives of those around you.

Read Romans 15:2. List one time you have spoken words that encouraged others.

Read Psalm 19:14. What is the psalmist saying he wants to be acceptable to the Lord? If that is your prayer, too, tell the Lord!

Read Matthew 12:35. Based on this verse and the one above, how do the words you plant in your heart result in the words you speak from your mouth?

Encourage Yourself

What do you do when the things in your life are challenging and difficult? Do you begin to think and speak negative words? King David experienced many trials during his life, and he did something that is worth noting: He encouraged himself in the Lord.

Read 1 Samuel 30:3-6 (Actually, you may enjoy reading this whole chapter—it is a great story!) What was the condition of David and his men when they found that their families had been captured?

What did the men want to do to David (see verse 6)?

What did David do in response to them (see verse 6)?

In the midst of the mourning and anger, David sought encouragement and strength from the Lord. He went to the One who held the final word over his difficult situation—and you can, too. You can find strength from the Lord, through His Word and in the words you speak to yourself during painful or depressing circumstances.

What words did David speak to himself? A quick trip through the psalms (David wrote nearly half of them) would suggest that he uttered his confidence in God's faithfulness.

Consider these passages.

"I love you, O Lord, my strength. The Lord is my rock, my fortress and my deliverer; my God is my rock, in Whom I take refuge. He is my shield and the horn of my salvation, my stronghold." Psalm 18:1-2 (NIV)

"Send forth Your light and Your truth, let them guide me; let them bring me to Your holy mountain, to the place where You dwell. Then I will go to the altar of God, to God, my joy and my delight." Psalm 43:3-4 (NIV)

"But my eyes are fixed on You, O Sovereign Lord; in You I take refuge—do not give me over to death. Keep me from the snares they have laid for me." Psalm 141:8-9 (NIV)

Having the right word at the right time is a precious and beautiful thing. As you turn your heart to the Lord through His Word, you can always find that right word. He is always ready to speak to you and to encourage you along in your walk with Him.

Proverbs 25:11 (NIV) says, "A word aptly spoken is like apples of gold in settings of silver."

What difficult situation are you facing right now that could use an "apt" word?

2.2 Far Reaching and Long Lasting

The effects of your words are far reaching and long lasting. Do you remember the illustration from the teaching of the Texas tree? Though relatively small in size, its root system was amazingly extensive.

In a similar way, the words you speak and the words you receive, though seemingly insignificant, ripple far beyond what you can immediately see. This is why it is so important that you take time to consider words in light of God's Word, and speak and receive only those that are helpful and good.

Speak and receive "blessings"—words that are in full agreement with the Word of God. Refrain from and reject "curses"—words that contradict the will of God as revealed in His Word.

Why speak words of life?

Good words *encourage* and build up those who hear them. Choosing your words carefully is important since their effects can be *far reaching* and *long lasting.* The right word at the right time in the right place can be a great blessing!

How do you

Speak Words of **Life?**

3.1 **Know the Lord... Test the Word**

You know that your words are seed and that these seeds are planted into the soul, which is the soil of everyone who hears them. You know that you can speak words that bring life instead of death; blessing instead of cursing. But how do you do this? How do you speak words of life? It begins by knowing the Lord.

Read John 10:1-6, 14, 27. Write out verse 4.

Why do the sheep follow the shepherd?

The sheep recognize the shepherd's voice because they *know* him. They spend a lot of time with him and realize that he is there to care for and protect them. Jesus makes it clear that this applies to His sheep as well. He is *the* Good Shepherd. As you grow in your relationship with the Lord, you will come to know Him more intimately and recognize His voice more clearly. This happens as you spend time with Him through Bible study and prayer.

Think of a close friend or family member. When they call you on the phone, do you recognize their voice? Why?

How well do you feel you know the voice of the Lord when He speaks to you?

Tell Him you would like to know His voice better.

Step #1—Determine the Source

When you hear words either spoken aloud or as thoughts in your mind, you can question the source—in other words, test the seed—before you choose whether or not to speak or personally receive it. This is why it is important that you *know* the Lord. God will not speak anything that contradicts what He has already given us in the Bible. Therefore, you can test the words to see what kind of seed they are. Words can come from your own flesh; they can come from the devil; or they can come from God.

Read John 8:44. What does the verse say about the nature of the devil's words?

How does this help you discern the source of the words you hear?

Read Psalm 19:7-11. List the adjectives used to describe God's Word (also referred to as His law, testimony, statutes, precepts, commands, judgments and ordinances).

Step #2—Accept or Reject the Word

Determining the source can help you decide whether to receive and retain the words spoken for yourself. It can also help you decide which words to speak to others.

The following chart may be helpful to you as you seek to test the source of the words you hear and speak.

Test the Words

Source	Evidence of Source	How to Respond
Are they from God?	Do they agree with what He has already said in the Scriptures?	*Receive, retain* and the word will *reproduce*
Are they from the flesh?	Do they lead you to selfish actions and attitudes?	*Reject* the word Or if the word has been received—*repent, remove* and *replace* with a blessing
Are they from the devil?	Do they slander or defame the Word of God or His character?	*Reject* the word Or if the word has been received—*repent, remove* and *replace* with a blessing

For example, the test might go something like this...because you know that the Lord's love for you never fails (see Jeremiah 31:3), you do not have to receive the words—spoken, thought, or felt—that He doesn't love you anymore. Since you know Him, you know that words of hopelessness and discouragement go against His nature as it is revealed in His Word. So you can conclude that the words are not from God and should not be received and retained, but rejected.

As you pass the words you hear through this grid, *accept* God's Word and *reject* those from your flesh or the enemy. God's Word will always build you up—helping you become the person He created you to be. These are the kind of words you should be speaking to those around you.

Apply this test with a word that has been spoken to you and a word that you spoke to another and write the results of the test below.

Word	Source/Evidence	Your Response
Spoken to you		
You spoke to another		

Choose to speak words of blessing. Know the Lord. Test the words. Speak and receive life!

3.2 Avoid Judgments...
Agreeing with the Word About the Work of God

Avoid Judgments

Have you ever thought you understood what someone was saying to you, only to find out that your assumptions were entirely incorrect? If you are like the rest of the human race, this probably has happened on several occasions. It is so easy to jump to conclusions. Part of learning how to speak words of life is learning to avoid making judgments about other people's motives and intentions.

In the teaching, you heard a story about a husband who would not open up to his wife, despite her desire to communicate. When he began to share, he became offended by something his wife did while listening to him. He interpreted her words and actions without asking her, and it caused him not to speak with her about anything significant for almost ten years! Surprisingly, when they finally uncovered the reason, it had to do with a misunderstanding that was not even close to his assumption. He had allowed incorrect thoughts in his mind to become facts; he planted seeds that were neither good nor helpful. It did not have to be that way. Note that your background, experience and even areas of sin and bondage can influence your interpretation or misinterpretation of what is spoken to you.

By avoiding judgments such as these, you can avoid a lot of unnecessary trouble! What is the solution to a situation like this? Ask! Simply take the time to humbly and prayerfully ask the person to explain what they were thinking.

Read Proverbs 15:28. What two paths can you take as you communicate with those around?

Be willing to extend grace to those around you. Reject thoughts that fill in the blanks for their heart or intentions. Instead, pray for them and commit to speaking words of life over them. Ask the Lord to enable you to be a blessing to them both with your actions and through your words.

Agreeing with the Word About the Work of God

Have you ever noticed that God is into the miraculous and unexpected? Sometimes He speaks to His people about plans that seem impossible. For example, your pastor may share an ambitious new strategy received during prayer to reach your entire city with the gospel by the end of the year. Or, a trusted friend may announce a leading from the Lord to leave the state and start a new business.

What do you do when things take a surprising turn and it appears that God is leading you or someone you love in a different and challenging direction? You have a choice: believe it by faith, despite your human reasoning, prayerfully submitting it to the Lord for confirmation; or to reject it because of fear and speak words against it. Let's take a look at a familiar Bible story and see what it says about speaking words of life over the work of God.

Read Numbers 13:1-2, 17-20, 25. What were the men sent to do?

Read Numbers 13:26-29. What was their observation about the land?

Read Numbers 13:30. What was Caleb's opinion about whether or not to take the land?

Read Numbers 13:31-33. What was the opinion of the others?

Read Numbers 14:1-4. How did the people respond to the bad report?

Read Numbers 14:26-30. What was the Lord's response to...

...the Israelites?

...Joshua and Caleb?

One report was prompted by *faith,* the other by *fear.* One report spoke words of life that brought encouragement, the other words of death that brought discouragement. As someone who is seeking to grow in the Lord and become more like Him, you must commit yourself to speaking words of life and avoid grumbling and complaining. This is a choice to walk in the Spirit, to depend upon Him for guidance and wisdom.

Read the following scriptures and briefly note what they say about grumbling and complaining.

☐ Philippians 2:14

☐ James 5:9

Realize that the roots of grumbling and complaining are fear and doubt. If you are not certain of how things will work out, you may fall back on faultfinding, hoping that if you find enough faults, the plan will be abandoned—just the like the spies that criticized the Promised Land. Certainly, you must prayerfully make plans in line with God's Word.

This is why you are learning to walk in the Spirit, to know the voice of the Shepherd and to step out in faith with whatever He brings to you. However, you must avoid making rash judgments about something or someone without taking the time to understand what is really going on. Avoid speaking out of fear and doubt.

Describe a time when you grumbled or complained.

*Now that you understand the effect of your words—***repent** *for speaking those negative words; ask the Lord to* **remove** *the power of them; and* **replace** *them by speaking words of blessing instead! Record those words of blessing here.*

When God reveals a specific plan to you or to someone in authority over you, such as a pastor or leader, take the time to pray about it before you jump to conclusions based solely upon your human reasoning or feelings. Walk in the Spirit, commit it to God and speak only words of life!

3.3 Taming the Tongue

Let's read from a book of the Bible that speaks loud and clear about the need to carefully consider what you say.

Read James 1:26. In light of this verse, how important is it to God that you keep a tight rein on our tongue?

Read James 3:2. What does this verse say about being a perfect or mature person?

Being able to always speak what is good and right is a huge and sometimes difficult task. The Bible is clear that it is a responsibility to take seriously. What you say really does matter, and in light of all you have studied so far, you can understand why. Now, how can you undertake the job of taming your tongue? Let's go to the Word and find out.

Read James 3:3-12. To what is the tongue compared in this passage?

A bit—a rudder—a spark, all three are so small yet have great power. All three cannot act independently; that is, someone has to control them in order to see their power manifested. Think about it. A bit is connected to reins both are controlled by a rider. A rudder is turned by the hand of the ship's captain. A spark is ignited by two elements striking against each other. Likewise, your words do not jump out of your mouth without some awareness of what is being spoken. This means that you can tame your tongue, so that it can be used to bring blessing and not destruction.

Match the scripture to the steps for taming your tongue.

Renew your mind to the Word.	John 14:26
Submit your mind to the Holy Spirit's counsel.	Romans 12:2
Stop speaking words of judgment.	James 3:17
Start speaking words of wisdom.	James 4:11

You tame your tongue by first taming your mind, the place where your thoughts originate and your heart, the place where your feelings originate. You tame your mind and emotions by immersing them in and adjusting them to the Word of God. It does not mean that every word you speak or receive must be a direct quote from Scripture.

Spend a few minutes and prayerfully consider if you have spoken words in a flippant or careless manner. Write them here.

Now, repent for those words you spoke. Ask the Lord to help you tame your tongue so that the words you speak are controlled and purposeful. Ask Him to continue to help you to walk in the Spirit in this area. Write what you prayed.

Rein. Steer. Ignite. But do so in the power of the Lord!

Do you remember the tube of toothpaste used as an object lesson during the teaching? Once it was squeezed out, there was no way to put it back. The same thing holds true for the words you speak: once you say them—blessing or cursing—they are out! If they are words of cursing, the only thing you can do is clean them up.

Death and life are in the power of the tongue! What fruit are you going to eat?

Speaking words of life does not mean that you will not be able to confront or challenge others. In fact, the Bible says that words of correction and discipline are an important part of spiritual growth. So, how do you know the difference between a critical and a correcting word? You think about the harvest that will be born as a result of what you have said or what has been said to you. Critical words end in judgment and condemnation. Correcting words, spoken in love, yield a harvest of right living.

Your words can produce death or life; speak words that produce life (see Proverbs 18:21).

Know the Lord so that you can discern His voice well.

Test the seed to determine if it is from God.

Avoid judging others; instead, bless them in word and deed.

Do not grumble or complain against the work of God.

But do deal with the words—*repent, remove,* and *replace* with a blessing!

Personal
Journal

Romans 15:4 tells us, "For whatever things were written before were written for our learning, that we through patience and comfort of the Scriptures might have hope."

Just as words of testimony were written down—words of failure were also recorded. Both teach those who are willing to learn. Let's apply this Biblical principle of learning from the past and gain hope by journaling about the following areas:

Record a time when you spoke words of life. _____

_____

_____

_____

What was the harvest? _____

_____

Record a time when you received words of life. _____

_____

_____

_____

_____

What was the harvest? _____

_____

Your Discipleship Assignments for this session are worship and Bible reading out loud—both great ways to speak words of life! Read the following scriptures out loud...

Psalm 105:1 (NIV) "Oh, give thanks to the Lord! Call upon His name; make known His deeds among the peoples!"

Psalm 117 (NIV) "Praise the Lord, all you Gentiles! Laud Him, all you peoples! For His merciful kindness is great toward us, and the truth of the Lord endures forever. Praise the LORD!"

...Then worship the Lord by singing a song to thank Him for the victory!

Record a time you spoke words that did not bring life. _____

_____

What was the source? _____

Record a time when you received words that did not bring life. _____

_____

What was the source? _____

If you have not already, **repent** of those words, ask the Lord to **remove** their effect and **replace** them by speaking blessing into that situation. Ask the Lord to help you in the future—remember, it is Him working in you to give you the desire and power to speak words of life (Philippians 2:13, NLT)!

Prayer
Commitment

What is your prayer regarding what you have learned and how you desire to put it into practice? This is a safe place to pour out your heart before the Lord. It is your chance...
...to ask for His strength and guidance and know He will give it!
...to express your fears and know He will help you overcome them!
...to make a commitment to speak words of life and know He will inspire them!
...to make a commitment to receive words of life and know He will give you discernment!

_____

_____

_____

_____

_____

_____

_____

Let this be a reminder of your commitment to the Lord and His covenant with you!

Signature _____ Date _____

During the Homework

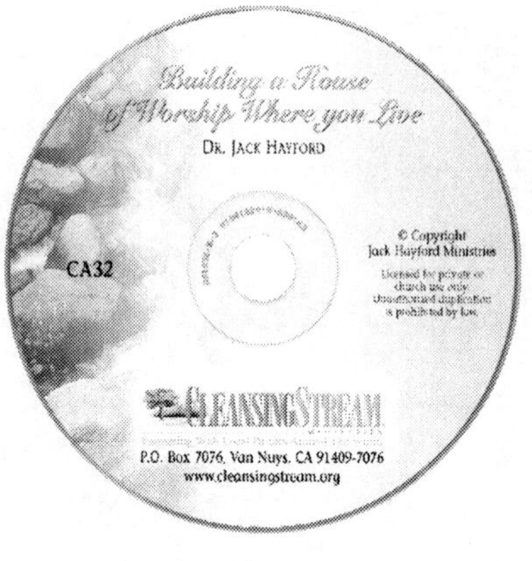

Building a House of Worship Where You Live Notes: ________

To Summarize:

Which truth had the greatest impact on you? ________

What was the most practical thing you learned? ________

How are you going to apply what you learned? ________

During the Homework

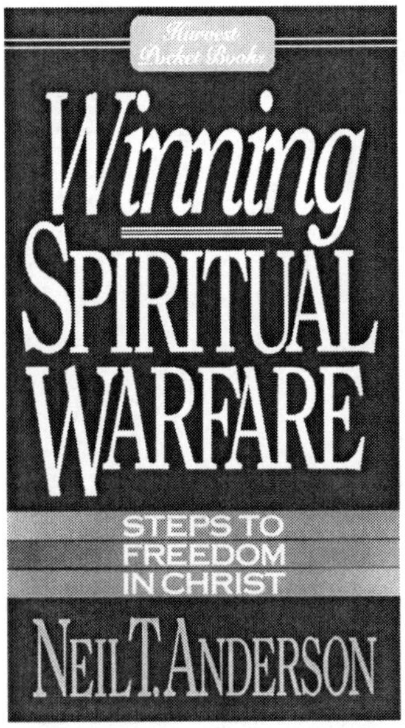
Harvest Pocket Books
Winning
SPIRITUAL
WARFARE
STEPS TO
FREEDOM
IN CHRIST
NEIL T. ANDERSON

Notes:

To Summarize:

Which truth had the greatest impact on you?

What was the most practical thing you learned?

How are you going to apply what you learned?

Session Four:

Enter the Cleansing Stream

If we confess our sins, He is faithful and just to forgive us our sins and to cleanse us from all unrighteousness.

1 John 1:9 (NKJ)

Session Four:

Enter the Cleansing Stream

Complete the following
homework assignments:

☐ **Workbook Section**
Enter the Cleansing Stream

☐ **Audio** teachings of
Devised for Your Defeat and
Prayer Loosing Sins Bondage
by Dr. Jack Hayford

Continue the previous
discipleship assignments:

☐ **Daily personal devotional
...Prayer
...Bible Reading** (see reverse)

☐ **Prayer partnership** with a
prayer partner or if married
with spouse

☐ **Regular attendance** in your
local congregation and at
the Cleansing Stream
Seminar Group

☐ **Worship** by singing a song
during your *devotional* and
before a *meal*

☐ **Bible Reading out loud:**
Couples: Husband reads the
second chapter to wife
Individuals: read second
chapter out loud

Add the following
discipleship assignments:

☐ **Daily putting on the
Armor of God**

☐ **Fast as the Lord directs**

© Copyright 2003 Cleansing Stream Ministries

Session Four:

Enter the Cleansing Stream

*If we confess our sins, He is faithful and just to forgive
us our sins and to cleanse us from all unrighteousness.*
1 John 1:9

Devotional Bible Reading

Week One

		Devotional	Out Loud
☐	Day 1:	Ephesians 1	Psalm 43
☐	Day 2:	Ephesians 2	Psalm 44
☐	Day 3:	Ephesians 3	Psalm 45
☐	Day 4:	Ephesians 4	Psalm 46
☐	Day 5:	Ephesians 5	Psalm 47
☐	Day 6:	Ephesians 6	Psalm 48
☐	Day 7:	Colossians 1	Psalm 49

Week Two

		Devotional	Out Loud
☐	Day 1:	Colossians 2	Psalm 50
☐	Day 2:	Colossians 3	Psalm 51
☐	Day 3:	Colossians 4	Psalm 52
☐	Day 4:	2 Timothy 1	Psalm 53
☐	Day 5:	2 Timothy 2	Psalm 54
☐	Day 6:	2 Timothy 3	Psalm 55
☐	Day 7:	2 Timothy 4	Psalm 56

About the Discipleship Assignment

Armor

Today the Lord is calling you to *Enter the Cleansing Stream*. As you do this you become aware that there is a battle going on. It isn't just what you see—it's deeper. The real battle is behind the scenes, in the heavenly places! Although the outcome has already been determined, through the cross and resurrection of Jesus Christ, you still have a part to play. When you accept the disciplines of wearing the armor received from the Lord and of fasting—you are equipped for battle!

Why put on the armor?

☐ Ephesians 6:10-13 says, *Finally my brethren, be strong in the Lord and in the power of His might.* **Put on the whole armor of God,** *that you may be able to* **stand against** *the wiles of the devil. For we do not wrestle against flesh and blood, but against principalities, against powers, against the rulers of the darkness of this age, against spiritual hosts in wickedness in the heavenly places. Therefore take up the whole armor of God that you may be able to* **withstand** *in the evil day, and have done all, to* **stand.**

☐ In this armor you can...

- ...*stand against* the enemy—aggressively opposing him.
- ...*wrestle* against the enemy—actively engaging him in one-on-one combat.
- ...*withstand*—the enemy and gain the victory!
- ...*stand*—after the battle is over to still be found standing!

How do you implement it?

☐ Through daily prayer put on each part of the armor and what it represents.

- v. 14 Belt of **Truth**
- v. 14 Breastplate of **Righteousness**
- v. 15 Shoes of the gospel of **Peace**
- v. 16 Shield of **Faith**
- v. 17 Helmet of **Salvation,**
- v. 17 Sword of the Spirit, which is the **Word of God**

☐ *Try it now.* "Lord I receive Your armor. I take the belt of truth. I choose to have everything held together by Your truth. I put on the breastplate of righteousness. May my heart and choices be guarded by righteousness. I place on my head the helmet of salvation. May the truth of my salvation help guard my thoughts. I take up the shield of faith—may it ever increase and defend against the enemy. I take the sword of the Spirit, which is the Word of God. May it help me discern between Your Spirit, my flesh and the enemy. May Your Word strengthen and encourage me all day today! And may Your Word reveal and defend against the lies of the enemy. I thank You for the provision of Your armor. In Jesus' name. Amen."

Fasting

Why fast and pray?

☐ Because...

- Jesus fasted (Matthew 4:2)
- The first Church fasted (Acts 13:2-3)
- Isaiah 58:6-7 talks about fasting—loosing bonds, undoing heavy burdens, setting the oppressed free, and breaking every yoke.
- In fact, Mark 9:29 tells us that some deliverance needs fasting, *...this kind can come out by nothing but prayer and fasting.*
- We do not fast to earn anything from God.
- But by fasting, you can walk a simple, dynamic pathway to spiritual conquest!

How do you implement it?

☐ *First, pray!* Fasting without prayer is simply going without food. It is not an issue of self-denial but an issue of waiting on God.

☐ Prayerfully consider joining Cleansing Stream in the three day fast scheduled before the retreat.

☐ Ask the Lord how to implement fasting, personally.

☐ If medical and dietary reasons prohibit fasting, then don't. Participate in the "spirit" of the fast by setting aside times of prayer beyond what you would usually do.

☐ For those who cannot do a total fast—drinking fruit juice helps to remain in the "spirit" of the fast

☐ If work requires high energy expenditure, consider a partial fast (i.e. Daniel 10:3 *no pleasant food*)

☐ Increase your intake:
- *Physically...* of water
- *Spiritually...* of the Word—Psalm. 19:10 says feed on it, *...Sweeter also than honey and the honeycomb.*

☐ AND PRAY! Use those times you would have been eating!

You are not called to a just survival mentality—God instead calls you to enter into the conflict, triumph, and see liberation happen personally and for others!

During the Teaching

What does it mean to *Enter* the Cleansing Stream?

Scriptures

(Laver) Exodus 30

If we confess our sins, He is faithful and just to forgive us our sins and to cleanse us from all unrighteousness.
1 John 1:9

Jesus said to him, "I am the way, the truth, and the life. No one comes to the Father except through Me." John 14:6

For we walk by faith, not by sight. 2 Corinthians 5:7

Looking unto Jesus, the author and finisher of our faith… Hebrews 12:2

Theme Scripture:

If we confess our sins, He is faithful and just to forgive us our sins and to cleanse us from all unrighteousness. 1 John 1:9

Definition:

"Enter" to choose

Quotes

What does it mean to *Enter* the **Cleansing Stream?**

Scriptures

We Enter... God Cleanses

_____
_____
_____
_____
_____
_____
_____
_____
_____
_____
_____
_____
_____
_____
_____
_____
_____
_____
_____
_____

Quotes

"Entering has to do with our choice - we confess our sins. Cleansing has to do with God and His choice – to forgive and to cleanse us."

What does it mean to enter the cleansing stream?

It is *your choice—you enter.* It is *God's choice—He provides cleansing.* You believe, He acts. You surrender, He restores. Are you ready?

Why *Enter* the Cleansing Stream?

The Enemy has a Plan and Wants a Place

Why *Enter* the Cleansing Stream?

Scriptures

...I have come that they may have life, and that they may have it more abundantly.
John 10:10

Nor give place to the devil.
Ephesians 4:27

God has a Plan... You have a Choice

_____
_____
_____
_____
_____
_____
_____
_____
_____
_____
_____
_____
_____
_____
_____
_____
_____
_____

Quotes

"No matter how it entered your life, whether you walked into it by your own choices, or you were born into it, or it was done to you as a victim. You have a choice—to continue to walk in it or walk away! You can make the choice to enter and God will meet you in the cleansing stream."

Why enter the cleansing stream?

The *enemy has a plan*—to steal, kill, and to destroy by keeping you in sin and bondage. Yes, there is a place, a place of influence—you can give to the enemy. But *God has a plan*—freedom, healing and abundant life! *It is your choice.*

How do you *Enter* the Cleansing Stream?

Scriptures

For God is working in you, giving you the desire to obey Him and the power to do what pleases Him.
Philippians 2:13 (NTL)

And you shall know the truth, and the truth shall make you free. John 8:32

If we confess our sins, He is faithful and just to forgive us our sins and to cleanse us from all unrighteousness.
1 John 1:9

The Process Begins... Restoring Relationship — Revelation... Repentance...

Quotes

_____
_____
_____
_____
_____
_____
_____
_____
_____
_____
_____
_____
_____
_____
_____
_____
_____
_____

How do you *Enter* the Cleansing Stream?

The Process Continues... Restoring Rulership — Renouncing... Restoration...

Scriptures

(Prodigal Son)
Luke 15:11-32 (NLT)

He who conceals his sins does not prosper, but whoever confesses and renounces them finds mercy.
Proverbs 28:13 (NIV)

...and to cleanse us from all unrighteousness. 1 John 1:9

Purify me from my sins, and I will be clean; wash me, and I will be whiter than snow. Psalm 51:7 (NLT)

Quotes

"Just like the prodigal son we can have a change of *mind*—coming to our senses, a change of *heart*—acknowledging our sin and a change of *will*—and go to our Father!"

"God has a table prepared for us and all we have to do is 'wash our hands.'"

How do you enter the cleansing stream?

Remember *God offers—you receive! You come—He cleanses.* The process of entering the cleansing stream is a partnership and it is clear (just remember the four R's).

- ☐ *Revelation*—seeing the truth of God's Word and allowing it and the Holy Spirit to identify areas of ongoing sin and bondage.

- ☐ *Repentance*—confession of the sin and turning from it back to God. The key is that sin is forgiven and the **relationship with God restored!**

- ☐ *Renouncing*—turning from the bondage, rejecting and breaking the influence of the enemy and **restoring God's rulership** in that area.

- ☐ *Restoration*—God cleanses and restores!

Then, you and He keep it clean!

In Summary:

What does it mean to enter the cleansing stream?

It is *your choice—you enter*. It is *God's choice—He provides cleansing*. You believe, He acts. You surrender, He restores. Are you ready?

Why enter the cleansing stream?

The *enemy has a plan*—to steal, kill, and to destroy by keeping you in sin and bondage. Yes, there is a place, a place of influence—you can give to the enemy. But *God has a plan*— freedom, healing and abundant life! *It is your choice*.

How do you enter the cleansing stream?

Remember *God offers—you receive!* You come—He cleanses. The process of entering the cleansing stream is a partnership and it is clear (just remember the four R's).

- ☐ *Revelation*—seeing the truth of God's Word and allowing it and the Holy Spirit to identify areas of ongoing sin and bondage.
- ☐ *Repentance*—confession of the sin and turning from it back to God. The key is that sin is forgiven and the **relationship with God restored!**
- ☐ *Renouncing*—turning from the bondage, rejecting and breaking the influence of the enemy and **restoring God's rulership** in that area.
- ☐ *Restoration*—God cleanses and restores!

Then, you and He keep it clean!

An Encouragement...

Anticipate God's plan for freedom and healing at the upcoming retreat!

Further Study

What does it mean to

Enter the Cleansing Stream?

Introduction

As you have been working through this workbook, others have been praying for you, and God has been moving in your life to teach you how to *Walk in the Spirit, Commit Everything to God* and *Speak Words of Life.* These lessons learned have helped to prepare you for the upcoming Retreat and beyond. Studying these truths may have also helped you identify areas of struggle. It would be easy to become discouraged and wonder if you will ever be able to consistently *Walk in the Spirit,* or *Commit Everything* (or even one thing) *to God* and not take it back, or *Speak Words of Life*—and not words that discourage.

You may have noticed as you progressed through the Seminar that God desires to walk with you. He is committed to you. He has many words to speak that will bring life to you, if you choose to receive them. You may not have done everything perfectly, but you have tried. So don't lose heart; there is an answer for ongoing areas of sin and struggle—God offers it—all we have to do is choose to receive what He offers!

Just as with a physical walk, you can get dusty and need a little cleaning up; when you walk on your journey with the Lord, you will discover that you need to stop from time to time to get "cleaned up" spiritually. That is what entering the cleansing stream is all about.

In this session we will be answering three main questions.
- ☐ *What* does it means to enter the cleansing stream?
- ☐ *Why* enter the cleansing stream?
- ☐ *How* do you enter the cleansing stream?

The key verse for this Session is 1 John 1:9. Write out this amazing, life-changing verse in the box—it will make you want to shout "Hallelujah!"

1 John 1:9

1.1 Enter Defined—You Come to Him, It's Your Choice

To begin, consider the word "enter." To enter something assumes that you are taking action to move from one place to another. It is a choice on your part. Allowing God to do a cleansing work in your soul also begins with a choice to move from one place to another—from where you currently are to where He is calling you to be. The point is that you can come if you choose to do so.

Read John 14:6. What is the only way to come to the Father?

People try many ways to connect with God, but the only way to reach Father God is through His Son, Jesus Christ. He is *the* way, the path to the Father and to wholeness. This may sound exclusive, but it is not. Why? Because *anyone* can come! All are loved and welcomed by the Lord. God will never turn away a seeking heart.

Read John 6:37. What is Jesus' response to whoever comes to Him?

Everyone is free to come; the key is to come in faith. That opens the door to the ongoing cleansing relationship with God.

Hebrews 11:6 (NIV) says, "Without faith it is impossible to please God, because anyone who comes to Him must believe that He exists and that He rewards those who earnestly seek Him."

Circle the word "faith." Underline the two things you must believe when you come to God.

The last part of Hebrews 11:6 says that you must come to God believing that He rewards those who seek Him. This means that God wants you to come anticipating that He will meet with you and that seeking Him ends in rich blessing. Sometimes you can, knowingly or unknowingly, assume that God is reluctant to touch you in a tangible, personal way, but He is not. He delights in those who earnestly seek Him. He loves to shower them with His love and goodness—and this includes you!

Have you ever felt reluctant about coming to God? Why or why not?

Look at Hebrews 4:16 in the versions following. Circle the words that describe how you are to approach God.

Hebrews 4:16 (NIV) says, "Let us then approach the throne of grace with confidence, so that we may receive mercy and find grace to help us in our time of need."

"Let us therefore come boldly to the throne of grace, that we may obtain mercy and find grace to help in time of need." (NKJV)

"Let us then fearlessly and confidently and boldly draw near to the throne of grace (the throne of God's unmerited favor to us sinners), that we may receive mercy [for our failures] and find grace to help in good time for every need [appropriate help and well-timed help, coming just when we need it]." (Amplified)

In each version underline the words that describe what the Lord extends to us. Remember, we just have to receive it!

Amazing "grace:" God's freely given love and favor—is offered—not condemnation. Wonderful "mercy:" God's kind treatment when punishment is deserved—is waiting—not judgment. God offered and you entered into a relationship with Him when you accepted Jesus as your Savior and your *spirit* was made alive.

God is offering again—and again it is your choice to enter to receive freedom and healing for your *soul*. Are you ready to make that choice to move forward and come to the One who loves you more than words can say?

Then tell Him so now—He has been expecting you!

1.2 Cleansing Stream Defined—It is God's Choice to Cleanse and Heal

What does it mean to "enter?" It is coming to God to receive what He is offering. What is the "cleansing stream?" It is a place of ongoing cleansing and healing. It is the place God has made available through the cross of Jesus and the payment made there. It is the place of God's grace and mercy. He desires to wash you in that life-giving stream and see you set free from everything that hinders or harms you. He wants His life—His abundant life—to touch you and envelope you with His perfect, heavenly love. He invites you to enter that place of cleansing. You have access through the blood of Jesus. Through Jesus' sacrifice, the curtain to God's presence has been opened wide to all those who will come.

Hebrews 10:19-23 says, 19 "Therefore, brothers, since we have confidence to enter the Most Holy Place by the blood of Jesus, 20 by a new and living way opened for us through the curtain, that is, his body, 21 and since we have a great priest over the house of God, 22 let us draw near to God with a sincere heart in full assurance of faith, having our hearts sprinkled to cleanse us from a guilty conscience and having our bodies washed with pure water. 23 Let us hold unswervingly to the hope we profess, for he who promised is faithful."

According to verse 19, what has God provided so you can "enter?"

According to verse 22, what must you choose to do?

Underline the truth in verse 23 that assures you the offer is good and you should choose to accept it.

4-17

Coming to Him in faith is like stepping into that stream and letting its cleansing power remove the sin and bondage bringing healing to the places of wounding. When you come to God in faith, He can take those areas of your soul you have been unable to get past or break free from—habits, family influences, sin, hurt, pain—and work a miracle. Encountering the presence of God will change you forever.

In the chart that follows, list one place in each area of your soul that you desire to see change but have not been able to experience breakthrough.

Areas of struggle in your soul (i.e. sin, bondage, generational influences, hurt, pain)
In your *mind*—an area of ongoing struggle with *thoughts:*
In your *heart*—an area of ongoing struggle with *feelings:*
In your *will*—an area of ongoing struggle with *choices:*

Tell the Lord you desire to enter and meet Him in the cleansing stream to receive His freedom and healing in these areas!

What does it mean to enter the cleansing stream?

It is *your choice*—you enter. It is *God's choice*—He provides cleansing. You believe, He acts. You surrender, He restores. Are you ready?

Why
Enter the Cleansing Stream?

2.1 Plans... A Place... A Choice

Why should you choose to enter the cleansing stream? Because wholeness and freedom are yours in Christ! By receiving what He has done for you, you can overcome ongoing sin and bondage, defeating the influence of the enemy in your soul!

The Enemy has a Plan and Wants a Place!

The enemy wants to keep you isolated from God—or at least make you *think* and *feel* you are isolated from Him. He starts with sin because he knows it will separate you from God.

Read the following scriptures and note what is said about sin.

☐ Isaiah 59:2

☐ Romans 3:23

The enemy knows that if we continue to sin in an area, we will be captured by it.

Read the following scriptures. Underline the words that describe what can happen if we continue to sin.

John 8:34 tells us, "Jesus answered them, 'Most assuredly, I say to you, whoever commits sin is a slave of sin.'"

Romans 6:16 says, "Do you not know that to whom you present yourselves slaves to obey, you are that one's slaves whom you obey, whether of sin leading to death, or of obedience leading to righteousness?"

Romans 7:23 says, "But I see another law in my members, warring against the law of my mind, and bringing me into captivity to the law of sin which is in my members."

Not only does the enemy want you to continue in sin and bondage, but once you are captured he seeks to keep you from getting cleaned up and free. Though the devil is a defeated enemy, he does not give up without a fight.

Write out Ephesians 4:27. Circle what you can give to the enemy.

This powerful little verse reveals a gigantic truth that, when understood, will give you the courage to walk to freedom. *You* have a choice. You can resist the devil and his soul-defeating plans. You can take away the place of influence in your soul.

Though your flesh pulls you to yield to its cravings and desires, though the enemy tempts you to cave into wrong choices, instead you can chose to yield to the Spirit and enjoy walking in freedom.

However, to defeat the darkness means that you must deal with the sins and bondage that are pressing in on you. The lie of the enemy is that you do not need to deal with sin; that you are okay just as you are. At first it sounds like an affirming word from the Lord: "You're fine. You don't need to change." Yet, just as you have to expose dirt to wash it off, you have to confess sin to see it forgiven.

Like dirt that you can see and needs to be washed away—there are open sins, such as complaining, gossip, profanity and immorality. Like germs that seem invisible but still need to be washed away—there are hidden sins such as unforgiveness, envy, lust, pride, hatred, or just not choosing to do what you know is right. Whether it is apparent or not, it is all sin and must be acknowledged in order to be dealt with and cleansed.

Read John 10:10. What three things does the devil, (the thief), come to do?

But what did Jesus come to give you?

Yes, there is a struggle. The devil pushes to see you robbed of God's blessings and joy; your own flesh cries out to go its own self-satisfying way; but Jesus wants you to experience life—life in the Spirit—abundant life! Unless you deal with ongoing sin by receiving God's cleansing and healing, you will suffer under its influence and bondage and it will distort your view of spiritual things. Ongoing sin and bondage that is not cleansed and removed will corrupt your soul and cause you to become blind and hardened to the truth of God. There is a way out: God has provided the place. It is your choice: darkness or light, sin or righteousness, bondage or freedom, brokenness or wholeness. What will you receive?

God has a plan!

God's plan has always been to see His people live in freedom and blessing. He created them to enjoy an intimate fellowship with Himself. Even when sin entered the world, He never stopped reaching out to His people. His love brought Jesus to earth to redeem and to restore people to fellowship with Him.

In the last section, you noted that the enemy comes to steal, kill and destroy. Your enemy wants to keep you separated from God through sin and bondage. But Jesus came to defeat the power of darkness over your life and to bring you back to God's original purpose for your life. Jesus clearly declared His mission as He was teaching in the synagogue one day.

Read Luke 4:18-21. List the things Jesus came to do.

Looking back at this list, circle the area you especially need to be touched by Him. Tell the Lord what you desire in that area.

It is important to note that when you accepted the gift of salvation, you were completely forgiven. God did not hold up a measuring stick next to you to decide how much of your sin to remove. No, the sacrifice of Jesus was complete.

Hebrews 10:10-14 (NIV) says, "And by that will, we have been made holy through the sacrifice of the body of Jesus Christ once for all. Day after day every priest stands and performs his religious duties; again and again he offers the same sacrifices, which can never take away sins. But when this priest had offered for all time one sacrifice for sins, he sat down at the right hand of God. Since that time he waits for his enemies to be made his footstool, because by one sacrifice he has made perfect forever those who are being made holy."

Notice the phrases "once for all" and "offered for all time one sacrifice for sins." What do they say about the sacrifice of Jesus?

If Jesus has "once for all" obtained *justification* for you, why do you still struggle with sin and bondage? Why do you need to come to Him for cleansing? Although your eternal salvation was secured by the sacrifice of Jesus, as you walk along in this broken world, you can make poor choices and slip into behavior that is outside of God's plan. You can get dirty again, sin—perhaps repeatedly—in an area and become entangled in bondage.

You may become hurt and refuse to allow it to be exposed, so that it can be cleansed and healed. You may become the victim of someone else's unredeemed nature. You may have experienced the influence of unrepented sin from past generations, pressing down on your generation. Everyone has family issues that are destructive and unsafe. All these things, while they do not affect your salvation, can keep your soul in bondage here on earth. This is where *sanctification* comes in. God wants you to be fully free—to bring every sin, bondage, wound, hurt or failure to the Cross, where He can cleanse your soul.

Again, it is important to understand the difference between justification and sanctification. Your spirit was completely justified when you accepted what Jesus did you for on the Cross. At that point you have been declared "not guilty" in God's eyes because of Jesus' death and resurrection. Now you must make daily choices to live as set apart to the Lord, learning to *Walk in the Spirit, Commit Everything to God, Speak Words of Life* and continue to implement the Discipleship Assignments like the two for this session—fasting and putting on the armor. This is all part of the sanctification process in your soul.

The story of Jesus raising Lazarus from the dead is a wonderful way to picture the truth of a soul's need for cleansing even after being saved. Lazarus was one of Jesus' friends. He died, and his sisters, filled with grief, begged Jesus to do something. Jesus went to the tomb and a miracle took place.

Read John 11:40-44. What did Jesus say after Lazarus had been raised from the dead and came out of his tomb (verse 44)?

Can you see the analogy? When you received salvation and forgiveness, life conquered death and you came out of your spiritual grave—like *justification*. But now the remains of that death, the grave clothes, must be taken off as well—in the ongoing process of *sanctification*.

You have a Choice!

This is why coming to the Lord for cleansing must be a regular part of your walk with Him. Come to God. Let Him wash you daily. You do not have to stay bound. Jesus came to give you abundant life, and all you must do to experience it is come—enter and receive the cleansing God offers.

When you enter, He *removes* what has bound you.

When you enter, He *releases* what has weighed you down.

When you enter, He *heals* areas of hurt and woundedness.

When you enter, He *renews* what has been lost or stolen.

Yes, you have a part—God does, too. Throughout the next four sections, you will look at each step in the process of deliverance and cleansing—and it is a process. Not one step has to be taken in your own strength. God has committed Himself to walk with you—to meet you in it—giving you all you need to receive His freedom and blessing.

Philippians 2:13 (NLT) tells us, "For God is working in you, giving you the desire to obey Him and the power to do what pleases Him."

Yes, you choose, but God is working in you! Underline the two things God gives you.

God gives you the desire to obey and the ability to come to Him. Since God is both working for you and in you, you can venture on the path with confidence and peace!

Why enter the cleansing stream?

The enemy has a plan—to steal, to kill and to destroy by keeping you in sin and bondage. Yes, there is a place, a place of influence—you can give to the enemy. *But God has a plan*—freedom, healing and abundant life! It is your choice.

How do you

Enter the Cleansing Stream?

3.1 The Process Begins... Restoring Relationship

Now it's time to consider *how* to enter and receive cleansing and healing. God calls you to move forward and to grow in your walk with Him, but then He kneels down, like a Father before a small child, and helps you do it. Let's begin the process with Him! It is a step-by-step process of **Revelation, Repentance, Renouncing** and **Restoration** (just remember the four R's). Ready to start? Let's take the first step!

Step #1: Revelation

James 4:8 says to, "Draw near to God and He will draw near to you..."

Begin the process of entering by seeking the Lord for revelation! Draw near to Him and listen.

Read John 8:32. What does it say is necessary for your freedom?

His Word, the truth, is essential. You need to see it, understand it, and use it to expose the lies of the enemy and reveal your sin. Because you cannot always see your own sin, ask the Lord to show you the areas the enemy has been able to muddy you with bondage and brokenness.

Read aloud Psalm 119:132-135 as a prayer asking God to reveal areas of sin and bondage in your life that He wants to see cleansed. Then consider each category listed on the next page and write down one

Area...	Revealed Sin
...Of failure?	
...Of sin?	
...Of hurts or wounds from other's actions?	
...Of family and friendships?	
...Of ambition and desires?	
...Other areas?	

Notes

Remember, *revelation* is seeing the truth of God's Word and allowing it and the Holy Spirit to identify areas of ongoing sin and bondage, which will lead to the next step!

Step #2: Repentance

James 4:8 calls you to, "... Cleanse your hands, you sinners; purify your hearts, you double-minded."

Remember, there is no condemnation in exposing things that need to be touched by God's cleansing power. Though it is difficult to do, it is the only way to freedom. God is with you and will walk you to victory.

This step calls for a response to what the Lord has revealed about your sin. It means agreeing with Him and being willing to repent, saying you are sorry. Through repentance—you *confess* the **sin** and *turn away* from it. The concept of "turning away" is very important. It is an act of your will. It is turning away from a pattern of sin in your life and going in the opposite direction, aligning yourself with God's will. Repentance deals with the sin and restores your relationship with God. But how?

1 John 1:9 says, "If we confess our sins, He is faithful and just to forgive us our sins..."

Circle what this verse tells you to do. Underline what God will do.

Confession is part of repentance and means to acknowledge your sin—admitting your guilt as a result of the conviction of your conscience, the Word and the Holy Spirit.

Read 2 Corinthians 7:9-10. What does godly sorrow lead to?

The conviction that comes from the Word and the Spirit will bring sorrow for your sin. It is your choice to repent, to say you are sorry. Acknowledge that your actions, attitudes and choices have gone against God's will as revealed by His Word and turn away from the sin toward God. Sometimes you do not realize that you have been on the wrong road. Once God shows you an area where you are walking on a different path, you must repent of it—turn and go the other way.

Jesus gave a great illustration of repentance in the Parable of the Prodigal Son found in Luke 15:11-24. Read this passage of Scripture and then answer the following.

Looking at verses 11-16, describe the state of the son when he left his father's house and then after living according to his way.

According to verses 17-19, what did the son do in response to the revelation of his true situation?

According to verses 20-24, how was he received by his father?

Complete the following chart. Indicate whether the prodigal son's action was: (1) revelation or (2a) repentance—confession of his sin or (2b) repentance—turning from his sin.

Verse	Change	(1) Revelation, (2a) Repentance—confession (2b) Repentance—turning
v. 17 (NIV) "he came to his senses"	Change of mind	
v. 18 "I have sinned"	Change of heart	
v. 18 "I will go to my father"	Change of will	

It is easy to slowly get stuck in the pigpen when you are walking according to your own way. But when you come to your senses—when the Holy Spirit awakens your heart to where you really are (revelation)—then you are in a position to do something about it (repentance)!

Just as the father forgave his prodigal son and received him back, so also our Heavenly Father will forgive us and receive us.

Read the following scriptures. Underline what is revealed about God's willingness to forgive your sin.

Isaiah 1:18 invites us to, "'Come now, and let us reason together,' says the Lord, 'Though your sins are like scarlet, they shall be as white as snow; though they are red like crimson, they shall be as wool.'"

Isaiah 44:22 declares, "I have blotted out, like a thick cloud, your transgressions, and like a cloud, your sins. Return to Me, for I have redeemed you."

Isaiah 55:7 says, "Let the wicked forsake his way, and the unrighteous man his thoughts; let him return to the Lord, And He will have mercy on him; and to our God, for He will abundantly pardon."

Want to read more? Try Psalm 103:12 and Hebrews 8:12.

When we repent of sin, the Lord will not only blot out the sin, but He will restore our relationship with Him. Are you ready for the restoration of that relationship? Then repent, and come receive forgiveness.

Spend a few moments in prayer, thanking God for providing for you, knowing you better than you know yourself and for giving you everything you need to choose to repent. Here's how!

Take one of the areas you identified during the section: 3.1 "The Process Begins—Step #1 Revelation" and now follow-through by repenting. Agree with the Lord, it is sin. Repent, confessing the sin, saying you are sorry and indicating your choice to turn from the sin back to the Lord. Jesus included repentance in the prayer He taught His disciples in Matthew 6:12 (NLT) "...forgive us our sins, just as we have forgiven those who have sinned against us." Your prayer might be something like this:

"Father God, I praise You that You are a God of revelation. I thank You for showing me my sin. I am sorry. Would You please forgive me? Thank You for Your forgiveness. Thank You for removing my sin because of Jesus. Thank You for restoring my relationship with You. I choose to turn from this sin to You! I love You and praise You for Your grace and mercy extended to me. In Jesus' name, Amen."

Or write your own prayer here.

Remember, *repentance* is confessing the sin and turning from it back to God. Your sin is forgiven and the relationship with God restored! Hallelujah! What good news!

3.2 The Process Continues...Restoring Rulership

Step #3: Renouncing

James 4:7 tells us to, "Submit to God. Resist the devil and he will flee from you."

Revelation exposes areas that need God's touch. *Repentance* acknowledges these areas. What is next? **Renouncing!** Renounce continues where repentance left off. In repentance you turned from the sin; in renouncing you turn from the *bondage,* rejecting the place of influence and returning to God's rulership.

To renounce something is to give it up by making a formal announcement that you turn away from the bondage and the spirit behind it. You break any agreements or connections with the bondage and the demonic spirit, removing its place of influence in your soul. You make a declaration to the Lord, the enemy and anyone else listening that you will have nothing more to do with it and are walking away from it forever.

Renouncing is not an attempt to try harder to stand against sin. Remember that Ephesians 4:27 tells you to *not* give a place to the devil. The word in the original Greek language for "place" is *topos* and literally means "land" or "ground." Once the devil has been given ground through unrepented or ongoing sin, it can become bondage in your soul. This is why it is so hard to "just stop sinning" in certain areas.

The good news is that you can take back any place the devil has gained influence in your life, whether it was through your choice or through the effects of someone else's choices on your life. How the enemy got hold of the ground is not the issue; God is able to drive him out regardless. The point for you is to recognize where the devil has bound you so that you can renounce the bondage, turn away from it and break its influence.

☐ Verse 11 "reckon yourselves to be dead indeed to sin"

☐ Verse 12 "do not let sin reign in your mortal body, that you should obey it in its lusts"

☐ Verse 13 "do not present your members as instruments of unrighteousness"

☐ Verse 14 "for sin shall not have dominion over you"

Proverbs 28:13 (NIV) says, "He who conceals his sins does not prosper, but whoever confesses and renounces them finds mercy."

Circle what happens when you confess (repent) and renounce a sin.

In the Lord's Prayer (see Matthew 6:13), Jesus gave us an example of how to pray. Write it here.

In the last section: 3.1 "The Process Begins—Step #2 Repentance," you repented for your sin in a specific area. Let's continue with the same area and **renounce**. *Your declaration might be something like this:*

I renounce (fill in the blank: i.e. anger, fear, unforgiveness). I reject your influence and break all agreements and connections with you. I break your influence over my life.

I choose to give God this place of rulership in my life!

Or write your own declaration here.

Someone once said you can "cancel the lease" the devil has on your life and take back every inch of ground he has stolen! It happens by God's grace when you enter the cleansing stream and you meet Jesus, the Deliverer, Who sets you free!

Renouncing deals with turning from the bondage, breaking the influence of the enemy and restoring God's rulership over that area.

Step #4: Restoration

James 4:10 calls us to, "Humble yourselves in the sight of the Lord, and He will lift you up."

Restoration is the final step in the process of entering the cleansing stream. This does not mean that *you* must figure out how to cleanse and rebuild, reconstruct, or restore the areas you brought before the Lord for cleansing and deliverance. You cannot do it. The Lord is the one who cleanses and restores.

Read 1 John 1:9. "If we confess our sins, He is faithful and just to forgive us our sins and…" complete the verse.

Who does the cleansing?

As God cleanses you, He removes what separates you from experiencing His full blessing. You will be free to walk with Him and to grow in your understanding of who He is and what He has for you as His child. This does not mean that you will never have to come to Him for cleansing again, though. Remember that your journey toward holiness is a process, and it requires a constant and steady obedience to the Lord.

Think back to the closing illustration from the teaching. As a child, did you ever try to come to the table with dirty hands? What was your parent's response? More than likely you heard, at least a thousand times, those four simple words: "Go wash your hands!"

The same is true for you as you run to the table of blessing God has set before you. You want to come in and immediately sit down and dig in, but God says, "Go wash first." Though you are saved and forgiven, you still must regularly bring areas before the Lord in which the dirt of the world and of sin has muddied you.

Being dirty does not mean you have lost your place at the table. It simply means that you need to get cleansed to fully enjoy what is set before you, and it happens by entering the cleansing stream.

Remember, *restoration* is God's job!

Read James 4:7-8, 10. Match each phrase or group of phrases in the chart with what it describes: Revelation, Repentance, Renouncing, or Restoration."

Scripture	Step in the Process
"Draw near to God and He will draw near to you."	Repentance
"Cleanse your hand, you sinners" "Purify your hearts, you double-minded"	Renouncing
"Therefore submit to God" "Resist the devil and he will flee from you"	Restoration
"Humble yourselves in the sight of the Lord" "He will lift you up"	Revelation

To see the Lord cleanse and restore, you must continually draw near to Him. Faithfully immerse yourself in His Word—let Him speak to you and you should regularly speak to Him in praise and prayer. In addition, this will keep you alert to the voice of our Good Shepherd and help you avoid the tactics of the thief. Abiding in Him and in His Word is essential (see John 8:31-32).

Read Ephesians 5:26. How are you cleansed?

Although this scripture addresses a husband's responsibility toward his wife, it also speaks about Christ's relationship with the Church, His Bride. The principle of the power of the Word of God to continually cleanse is clear.

Read 3 John 4. How does this describe the heart of God?

God loves you so much He refuses to let you wallow in the mud. He reaches down and takes your hand and gently draws you to a place where He can restore you. Thank God for His amazing gift of forgiveness and cleansing!

Remember, *God offers—you receive!* You come—He cleanses. The process of entering the cleansing stream is a partnership, and it is clear (just remember the four R's).

□ *Revelation*—seeing the truth of God's Word and allowing it and the Holy Spirit to identify areas of ongoing sin and bondage.

□ *Repentance*—confession of the sin and turning from it back to God. The key is that sin is forgiven and the **relationship with God restored!** Hallelujah! What good news!

□ *Renouncing*—turning from the bondage, rejecting and breaking the influence of the enemy and **restoring God's rulership** in that area.

□ *Restoration*—God cleanses, heals and restores!

Then, you and He keep it clean together!

The purpose of these previous four sessions has been to ready your heart for the good work God wants to do in you at the Retreat and beyond. In addition, as you prepare for the upcoming Retreat, the Discipleship Assignments for this session will help you. Take the time to read about fasting and putting on the armor of God. As you implement these disciplines, your soul is prepared, and they become weapons against the enemy to remove his influence in your life!

Look back at the specific areas you listed under the section: 3.2" The Process Begins—Step #2 Repentance. Now that you better understand the process, refine what you wrote down into concise, specific events or areas. If something else has come to mind, include it as well.

Area of failure: _____

_____

_____

Area of sin: _____

_____

_____

Area of hurts or wounds from the others' actions: _____

_____

_____

Area of family and friendships: _____

_____

_____

Area of ambitions and desires: _____

_____

_____

Other areas: _____

_____

_____

_____

_____

God is with you, inviting you to receive His cleansing and healing in all of these areas. Remember, the purpose of entering the cleansing stream and dealing with painful and difficult areas of sin and hurt in your life is so that you can enjoy the freedom and joy God intended. With this in mind, you can rejoice and know that God is not finished yet. He has a wonderful future in store for you as you continue to follow Him.

Prayer

Commitment

Tell the Lord that you desire to enter and meet Him for cleansing and healing. Tell Him the areas where you desire cleansing and healing (you can write them here or mark your previous list).

_____

_____

_____

_____

_____

_____

_____

Remember, Philippians 1:6 (NIV) says, "Being confident of this, that he who began a good work in you will carry it on to completion until the day of Jesus Christ."

God always finishes what He starts. Write a prayer of thanksgiving for what He has begun and for what He will continue to do at the Retreat and beyond as you walk obediently before Him.

_____

_____

_____

_____

_____

_____

Let this be a reminder of your commitment to the Lord and your gratefulness for His covenant with you!

Signature _____ Date _____

During the Homework

Devised
for Your Defeat
Dr. Jack Hayford

CA45

© Copyright
Jack Hayford Ministries

Licensed for private or
church use only.
Unauthorized duplication
is prohibited by law.

CleansingStream
P.O. Box 7076, Van Nuys, CA 91409-7076
www.cleansingstream.org

Devised for Your Defeat Notes: _____

_____

_____

_____

_____

_____

_____

_____

_____

_____

_____

_____

To Summarize:

Which truth had the greatest impact on you? _____

_____

_____

_____

What was the most practical thing you learned? _____

_____

_____

_____

How are you going to apply what you learned? _____

_____

_____

_____

During the Homework

Prayer Loosing Sins Bondage Notes: _____

_____

_____

_____

_____

_____

_____

_____

_____

_____

_____

_____

_____

_____

To Summarize:

Which truth had the greatest impact on you? _____

_____

_____

What was the most practical thing you learned? _____

_____

_____

How are you going to apply what you learned? _____

_____

_____

About the Retreat

We invite you to join us at a Regional Retreat!

You have come so far, pressed through so much, and are on the verge of something amazing. Your attendance at the Regional Retreat is an integral part of the Seminar and should not be missed by anyone! It is an exciting yet tender time where you join with others in the greater Body of Christ to worship, hear truth, and receive ministry unto freedom and healing—all to the glory of God!

Session Five:
Press
Toward the Goal

*...forgetting what lies behind
and reaching forward
to what lies ahead,
press on toward the goal
for the prize of the upward call
of God in Christ Jesus.*
Philippians 3:13-14 (NASB)

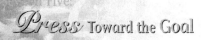

Session Five:
Press Toward the Goal

Complete the following homework assignments:

☐ **Workbook Section**
Press Toward the Goal

☐ **Book**
Protecting Your Home from Spiritual Darkness
by Chuck Pierce and
Rebecca Wagner Sytsema

Continue the previous discipleship assignments:

☐ **Daily personal devotional**
...Prayer
...Bible Reading (see reverse)

☐ **Prayer partnership**

☐ **Regular attendance**

☐ **Worship**

☐ **Bible Reading out loud**

☐ **Daily putting on the Armor of God**

☐ **Fast** as the Lord directs

Add the following discipleship assignments:

☐ **Cleansing** – *putting your house in order*

☐ **Covering** – *setting your home apart for the Lord*

© Copyright 2003 Cleansing Stream Ministries

Session Five:
Press Toward the Goal

*...forgetting what lies behind and reaching forward
to what lies ahead, I press on toward the goal
for the prize of the upward call of God in Christ Jesus*
Philippians 3:13-14 NASB

Devotional Bible Reading

Week One

		Devotional	Out Loud
☐	Day 1:	Galatians 5	Psalm 57
☐	Day 2:	Hebrews 1	Psalm 58
☐	Day 3:	Hebrews 2	Psalm 59
☐	Day 4:	Hebrews 3	Psalm 60
☐	Day 5:	Hebrews 4	Psalm 61
☐	Day 6:	Hebrews 5	Psalm 62
☐	Day 7:	Hebrews 6	Psalm 63

Week Two

		Devotional	Out Loud
☐	Day 1:	Hebrews 7	Psalm 64
☐	Day 2:	Hebrews 8	Psalm 65
☐	Day 3:	Hebrews 9	Psalm 66
☐	Day 4:	Hebrews 10	Psalm 67
☐	Day 5:	Hebrews 11	Psalm 68
☐	Day 6:	Hebrews 12	Psalm 69
☐	Day 7:	Hebrews 13	Psalm 70

Putting your House in Order

Cleansing

Today the Lord is calling you to continue the journey...to *Press Toward the Goal.* Now that you have received cleansing and healing, welcoming the Lord in a greater dimension into your life... you also need to look to your home. Putting your home in order by removing anything that does not bring glory to God, AND setting it apart for Him—inviting His presence in a fresh way. I guess you could call it "cleansing and covering!" Although these are listed as two Discipleship Assignments they are to be done at the same time—cleanse then cover!

Why put your house in order?

- First Corinthians 5:6-8 warns you that a little leaven affects the whole lump and calls you to remove it.
  - That means looking for and removing anything unclean, impure, evil, or just carnal.
  - This scripture tells you it doesn't take much—just a little to have an affect.
- You want everything in your home to glorify God—not just your possessions, but your speech and actions as well.

How do you implement it?

- Pray and ask the Lord to show you who to pray with and when to pray
- Follow through and set it up!
- Pray cleansing through your house from the outside in...
  - ... with family or friends
  - ... around the property
  - ... room by room
- Pray and ask the Lord what needs to be cleansed or removed
- Ask Him what to do and do it!
- Continue to be open to the Holy Spirit and His leading to periodically pray cleansing

About the Discipleship Assignment

Setting your Home apart for the Lord
Covering

Why set your home apart?

- ☐ Throughout the Bible, God has given land and the responsibility to possess it to his people.
  - ▪ In Genesis 13:17 Abraham was told to, *Arise, walk in the land through its length and its width, for I give it to you.*
  - ▪ In Joshua 1:2-3, *The children of Israel were told, Now therefore, arise... every place that the sole of your foot will tread upon I have given you.*
  - ▪ As you possess the land given to you then you can set it apart for the Lord, welcoming His rule and reign there.

How do you implement it?

- ☐ By consecrating your houses to the Lord now
- ☐ Walk around the property—outside and inside
- ☐ As you do, prayerfully consider incorporating...
  - ▪ ... praise and worship
  - ▪ ... prayer
  - ▪ ... the Word
  - ▪ ... communion
- ☐ Continue to be open to the Lord's leading to periodically pray covering over your home

Preparing a place for the Lord and inviting Him not only into your heart but also your home will be rewarded. God will always come to abide where people align their hearts with His throne.

During the Teaching

What does it mean to *Press* Toward the Goal?

Scriptures

(Possess the Land)
Deuteronomy 8:2

Theme Scripture:

Not that I have already obtained it or have become perfect, but I press on so that I may lay hold of that for which also I was laid hold of by Christ Jesus. Brethren, I do not regard myself as having laid hold of it yet; but one thing I do; forgetting what lies behind and reaching forward for what lies ahead, I press on toward the goal for the prize of the upward call of God in Christ Jesus.
Philippians 3:12-14 (NASB)

Definition:

"Goal"– Greek word *skopos:*
    Used in classics as a mark for shooting at
    Used as a moral or intellectual end
    A goal which controls his life

"Press"– Greek work *dioko:*
    To follow or press hard after
    To pursue with earnestness and diligence to obtain
    To run swiftly in order to catch a person or thing

Quotes

"The process is just as important as where you are going."

"My goal will control my life."

_____

_____

_____

_____

_____

_____

What does it mean to press toward the goal?

To diligently pursue Jesus and His call.

Why *Press* Toward the Goal?

Scriptures

Before I formed you in the womb I knew you, and before you were born I consecrated you; I have appointed you a prophet to the nations.
Jeremiah 1:5 (NASB)

Eternal... Unique... Design Assignment

Quotes

"There is an eternal reason for your existence."

"There is a unique reason for your existence."

"There is a design assignment for your life."

Why press toward the goal?

Because in doing so you will fulfill your God-ordained *destiny:* a life of freedom, rich with His blessing and presence.

How do you *Press* Toward the Goal?

Scriptures

(Written for our instruction)
Romans 15:4

(Whoever seeks his own way)
Proverbs 18:1

But we all with unveiled face beholding as in a mirror the glory of the Lord, we are being transformed into the same image from glory to glory, just as from the Lord the spirit.
2 Corinthians 3:18 (NASB)

(Moses) Exodus 34:29-35

(Jesus choose 12)
Mark 1:14-20; 2:13

(Work as working for the Lord)
Colossians 3:23

Follow Biblical Characters...
Enjoy the Journey...
Realize Your Need for Others

Quotes

"Press Toward the Goal by following the example of Biblical characters... by enjoying the journey not just the destination... realizing your need for significant others in your life."

How do you *Press* Toward the Goal?

Thank-full... Word-full—Person

Scriptures

(In everything give thanks)
1 Thessalonians 5:18

Enter His gates with thanksgiving and His courts with praise. Give thanks to Him, bless His name.
Psalm 100:4 (NASB)

(Word of God is living)
Hebrews 4:12-13

(Plumb line) Amos 7:1-8

(Children, husband, wives)
Ephesians 5:22-6:4

(Word hid in my heart)
Psalm 119:11 (KJV)

Quotes

"The manufacturer gave us a handbook and we need to follow it."

"I don't measure the Bible by what I do; I measure what I do by the Bible."

How do you *Press* Toward the Goal?

(Without faith it is impossible to please God) Hebrew 11:6

(Ask anything)
1 John 5:13-14

(Lord's prayer) Luke 11:2

And do not get drunk with wine... but be filled with the Spirit...
Ephesians 5:18 (NASB)

(Come let us reason together)
Isaiah 1:18-19

But I say, walk by the Spirit, and you will not carry out the desire of the flesh.
Galatians 5:16 (NASB)

Faith-full... Spirit-full—Person

Quotes

"Faith is adjusting my feelings to the facts."

"If God said it, I am obligated to believe it."

"Are you full of the Spirit? Get topped off!"

How do you *Press* Toward the Goal?

Brand new... Cleansed... Serving—Person

Scriptures

(Put off the old, put on the new) 2 Corinthians 5:17

Acts 19

(Keep him in perfect peace) Isaiah 26:3

(It is more blessed to give than to receive) Acts 20:35 (NASB)

(The good that you make happen for others, God will make happen for you.) Ephesians 6:7-8 (paraphrase)

Until I come, give attention to the public reading of Scripture, to exhortation and teaching. Do not neglect the spiritual gift within you, which was bestowed on you through prophetic utterance with the laying on of hands by the presbytery. Take pains with these things; be absorbed in them, so that your progress will be evident to all. Pay close attention to yourself and to your teaching; persevere in these things, for as you do this you will ensure salvation both for yourself and for those who hear you.
1 Timothy 4:13-15 (NASB)

Quotes

"You're a brand new person—put off the old and put on the new!"

"Keep your temple free. Keep your relationships unfettered. Keep your mind stayed on Him."

"Becoming is a life-long process"

How do you press toward the goal?

Continue the journey by becoming a *thank-full, Word-full, faith-full, Spirit-full* and a *brand new, cleansed* person... by putting your house in order through *cleansing* and *covering*... and by being *released to serve* with a humble heart!

In Summary:

What does it mean to press toward the goal?

To diligently pursue Jesus and His call.

Why press toward the goal?

Because in doing so you will fulfill your God-ordained *destiny:* a life of freedom, rich with His blessing and presence.

How do you press toward the goal?

Continue the journey by becoming a *thank-full, Word-full, faith-full, Spirit-full* and a *brand new, cleansed* person... by putting your house in order through *cleansing* and *covering...* and by being *released to serve* with a humble heart!

Further Study

What does it mean to
Press toward the Goal?

Introduction

In the last few months, you have learned several important Biblical truths which have enabled you to address areas of influences and bondage.

☐ In Session One: *Walk in the Spirit*—You learned about keeping your feet on the right path by walking in step with the Holy Spirit.

☐ In Session Two: *Commit Everything to God*—You learned that continuing on that path requires committing everything to Him, daily trusting in His love and goodness.

☐ In Session Three: *Speak Words of Life*—You brought your words under the light of His Word and embraced the command of Scriptures to speak and receive words of life.

☐ In Session Four: *Enter the Cleansing Stream*—You washed in the cleansing stream God provided that brings freedom and wholeness.

Interwoven with these life-changing truths, you were challenged to embrace spiritual disciplines that, when incorporated into your daily life, become habits through which the Lord continues His good work.

Attending the Seminar and Retreat is not the end—it is just the beginning! In this last session, we will be answering three questions:

☐ What does it means to press toward the goal?

☐ Why press toward the goal?

☐ How do you press toward the goal?

The key verse for this study is Philippians 3:12. Write it out below and underline the words "I press on."

Philippians 3:12

Do you want to continue growing in the Lord? Then you are in the right place!

1.1 Press Defined

A quick look at two Greek words will fine-tune our understanding of what it means to press toward the goal. Put on your scholar's cap and get ready!

The word "press" in Greek (the language of the New Testament writings) is the word *dioko*. "Dioko" means to follow hard after something, pursuing it. It also means to run swiftly to catch something or someone.

The Greek word "goal" in Philippians 3:14 is *skopos* and has to do with "seeing" something. Words such as "telescope" and "periscope" come from this Greek word. As it is used in the Bible verse, it means the mark or target you are seeing ahead of you, the goal for which you are aiming.

Rewrite the key verse and replace the words "press" and "goal" (or some translations use the word "prize") with the above definitions.

To "press toward the goal" means that you see the target of an intimate relationship with God in front of you and pursue it with earnest diligence. You are not pursing healing, faith, deliverance, or blessing. You are pursuing *Jesus*. It means to focus on Him and to earnestly and faithfully pursue Him. And as you come to Him, you find everything you need. Remember it the journey—not just the destination—that is important.

Read Philippians 3:13-14. According to verse 13, what are you to forget?

What are you to reach for?

What does it mean to press toward the goal?
To diligently pursue Jesus and His call.

Why *Press* toward the Goal?

2.1 Fulfill Your God-Ordained Destiny

As you press toward the goal God has set before you, you will come to understand and enjoy the reason for which He created you. You will move forward in fulfilling your destiny in Christ.

Read aloud Psalm 139:16. What was written before you were even born?

What does this say about your worth and value to God?

Read John 15:14-16. What does it mean that Jesus calls you a friend?

How is that different than being His servant?

The most compelling reason to press toward the goal is so you can enjoy a deeper relationship with the One Who both created and loves you. God invites you to partner with Him as a friend, to see His will established on the earth. Though He did not *need* you, He desired you and made a way for you to walk alongside Him, just as by His Spirit He walks alongside you. Having just attended the Retreat, you are at a place of freedom and healing—poised to continue the walk. This freedom needs to be tended with consistency and watchfulness and established with persistence. This tending happens as you faithfully press toward Him.

Read 1 Corinthians 9:24-27. Notice the words "do not run aimlessly" (NIV—other versions use "with uncertainty") in verse 26. What does this passage say about the commitment of an athlete as they train?

Why is discipline and focus so important?

Read Hebrews 12:1-2. Notice the words "run with endurance" (NIV—other version use "perseverance") in verse 1. Note what we are to lay aside and what we are to focus on in the following chart.

Lay aside...	Focus on...

You may make mistakes and stumble along the path, but the important thing is to be like an athlete running in a competition: get up and keep going. That athlete runs despite the distractions, obstacles, or assaults along the way. You must do the same. Keep pressing forward. Hold tightly to the work God has done in you and earnestly pursue the work He wants to continue to do in you.

Read Galatians 6:9. According to this verse, what will happen if you don't quit?

God has a divine plan for your life. He created you for a specific purpose. As you press on to know Him and to walk in freedom and wholeness before Him, you will find Him directing your life into the plans He made for you before you were even born. That is why you must press toward the goal—choice-by-choice!

Why press toward the goal?

Because in doing so, you will fulfill your God-ordained *destiny:* a life of freedom and fulfillment, rich with His blessing and presence.

How do you *Press* toward the Goal?

3.1 Continue the journey...
Be Transformed from Glory to Glory

Okay, you know what it means to press toward the goal and why it is so important that you do. Now, let's get down to the practical "how-to's." *How* do you press toward the goal? Think back to the teaching. Do you remember the story about the sign that hung in the seamstress' window? It said: "If your clothes aren't becoming to you, you should be coming to us." This funny little advertisement is really the answer to how you press toward the goal. Come to God—simple, but true. It all boils down to this: your need to daily connect with the One who brought you to freedom and healing. Coming to Him is your responsibility. This is how you press.

So, how do you *come?* You come through Bible study, prayer, worship, fellowship—any way He draws you closer to Him! God will transform you from glory to glory, and you will become more and more the person He created you to be. There will always be areas in your life in which God is working, but every time you come, He works. The point is that you come.

The Bible gives continual encouragement to press toward the goal. Each time you read, you can drink in words inspired by the Holy Spirit (see 2 Peter 1:20-21) and be continually refreshed by God. God created you for fellowship, and this is the purpose for the Word—both written and living—working in your life. He desires you and placed in you a desire for Him. He instilled in your soul a longing for His presence that nothing else can satisfy. As you yield to this design and come to Him, you will experience transformation.

Read 2 Corinthians 3:18. According to this verse, into whose likeness are you being transformed?

How are you being transformed?

Who does the work of transformation?

The Bible gives many examples of people who followed God and accomplished great things for Him. It also tells of those who, through disobedience, did not fulfill His plan. Romans 15:4 tells us that we can learn something from both examples.

Read Romans 15:4. What two things do the Scriptures give us?

Think of a biblical character whose perseverance brought about God's plan in their life. How does their life serve as an example to you? (If you can't think of one, you can read the story of Joseph in Genesis 37-47.)

Think of a biblical character whose disobedience kept them from fulfilling God's plan. How does their life serve as an example to you? (If you can't think of one, you can read the story of Rehoboam in 1 Kings 12:1-17.)

Your identity is not in what you do, but in who you are; it is not in your accomplishments, but in your relationship with the Lord. Each time you come into His presence, you are changed. This is the ongoing process of sanctification that you learned about when you studied *Walk in the Spirit*. Each day that you continue to press, coming toward Him, you grow in Christ-likeness. Each time you are in His presence, you are changed from glory to glory.

Do not be discouraged if you are not today the person you hope to be. Keep pressing toward the goal. Keep coming into the presence of the Lord. He will continue to reveal and change, to unveil and transform, until the day you stand before Him face to face. The Bible says, "...Now I know in part; then I shall know fully, even as I am fully known" (1 Corinthians 13:12, NIV). Continue to press forward by surrendering your soul to the ongoing transforming work of the Holy Spirit. Press toward the goal.

3.2 Thank-full...Word-full Person
Become a Thank-full Person

There are several distinctive attributes of person who is being transformed by the Word, who is pressing on toward the goal. One of these attributes is thankfulness. Why? Because thankfulness is faith's voice! It is the song of those who believe that He is faithful to His Word and to His work.

Look up the following verses and briefly note what they say about being thankful.

☐ Psalm 95:1-2

☐ 1 Thessalonians 5:18

Thankfulness is not blind optimism, nor is it a fruit of the Spirit. Thankfulness is your choice. It is your response to who God is and what He has done, is doing and will do. When your eyes are on your labor, your effort, yourself, you won't be able to sink into humble gratefulness for Him, His labor and work. When you consider what God has done for you, when you realize just how good He really is, you cannot help but respond to Him with deep gratitude and joy.

Consider the following verses—what are you to be thankful for?

☐ 2 Corinthians 2:14

☐ 2 Corinthians 9:15

What are three specific things regarding God's working in your life right now that you are thankful for?

How do you become a thankful person? Begin by looking at Him. Thankfulness is not about having, but about knowing—and you have been given an open door to know Father God, His Son and His Spirit through Jesus' sacrifice. What God gives to you, He gives because of who He is, not because of what you do.

Read Psalm 136 aloud.

Notice a common theme? How about: "Give thanks to the Lord for He is good! His love endures forever" (NIV). Now that is something to be thankful for! God is your Creator, Sustainer, Deliverer and Redeemer—and His intense love for you will never fade away or burn out. It lasts forever!

Match the following sections from Psalm 136 with the corresponding statements.

Psalm 136:5-9	Thank God that He's your Protector
Psalm 136:10-15	Thank God that He's your Sustainer
Psalm 136:16	Thank God that He's your Creator
Psalm 136:17-20	Thank God that He's your Guide
Psalm 136:21-22	Thank God that He's your Redeemer
Psalm 136:23-24	Thank God that He's your Deliverer
Psalm 136:25	Thank God that He's your Provider

One way to keep this heart of thankfulness is to sing your praises to the Lord. Both Colossians 3:16 and Ephesians 5:19 encourage believers to sing their thankfulness. First Peter 2:9 says to "proclaim the praises of Him who called you out of darkness into His marvelous light." Songs often communicate your heart in ways that words alone cannot.

Think of a worship song you know that declares how great and how good God truly is. Write down the words or a key phrase from that song. Now take a moment and sing it aloud to Him.

Become thankful. Focus on Who He is and what He has done. He is good!

Become a Word-full Person

Another essential to pressing toward the goal is to become a person of the Word. It is impossible to be transformed by the Word if you never read it! This means that you fill your heart and mind with the truths of Scripture so much that His Word spills over into every area of your life.

Through the Discipleship Assignments, you have already taken this vital truth to heart. You know that spending time each day in Bible reading, both silently and aloud, is the foundation for a growing walk with God. Along with your personal Bible study, you also benefit from hearing the Word preached and taught as you fellowship with other believers. You need to consistently receive the Word.

Write out 2 Timothy 3:16-17.

Circle the four ways the Word of God impacts your life.
Underline the result of the Word working in you according to verse 17.

When the Bible says that it is "God-breathed," it means that the Word was produced by the creative breath of God. His life is in each book; His Spirit is in every line. Bible reading, both silently and aloud, is a vital habit for continued spiritual growth! Why? When you read the Bible, God's thoughts and wisdom wash over you and you stay cleansed and focused (see Ephesians 5:26). But just reading the Word is not enough; you must obey it—putting it into practice—making it a part of your life.

James 1:22-25 (NLT) says, [22]"And remember, it is a message to obey, not just to listen to. If you don't obey, you are only fooling yourself. [23]For if you just listen and don't obey, it is like looking at your face in a mirror but doing nothing to improve your appearance. [24]You see yourself, walk away, and forget what you look like. [25]But if you keep looking steadily into God's perfect law—the law that sets you free—and if you do what it says and don't forget what you heard, then God will bless you for doing it."

According to verses 23-24, what does it say about reading the Word but not doing what it says?

According to verse 25, when we keep looking into God's perfect law and do what it says, what happens in our lives?

The Bible is the *only* standard we have for maintaining accurate beliefs about God and the way He wants us to live our lives. His Word is His revelation to us, and we must embrace it daily in order to see growth spiritually. The Bible is not just an old book with good advice: it is the very Word of God Himself and is able to speak to you with absolute authority. It is the *only* standard for faith and practice.

Are you up for a Bible challenge? Psalm 119 is a lengthy song extolling the blessing and necessity of the Word of God. Read through the whole psalm—it will take some time, but it is worth it! When you have finished, choose one section (they are grouped in most Bibles into eight verse segments), and reread it aloud. Then, for each verse, write down the verse and how the Word works in your life in the following chart. For example, if you chose the second section, verses 9-16, you might fill in the chart for verse 9 as noted.

Verse(s)	How the Word Works
v. 9	Living according to the word keeps me PURE

Romans 12:2 explains that you are transformed by the renewing of your minds. When you allow His thoughts to replace yours, His wisdom to become yours, your mind is being made new—the way it was intended to be. For this reason, you should never be fearful of holding your life under the magnifying glass of the Word. Allowing the Word to examine your life is how you allow the Lord to change you.

You must become full of the Word. To press toward the goal requires submission to the Word.

3.3 Faith-full...Spirit-full Person
Become a Faith-full Person

Thank-full. Word-full. What is next? Another key characteristic of someone who is pressing toward the goal is that they are faith-full. Have you ever stopped to consider what the word "faithful" means? Perhaps the words "reliable" or "dependable" come to mind—and someone who is faithful certainly has these qualities. "Faithful" literally means "full of faith." To be faithful, then, is to live with certainty and conviction (i.e., faith) that steadies your course and makes your actions and responses predictable (i.e., dependable). Can you see how this relates to pressing toward the goal? Without faith you will wander instead of march; you will roam instead of press. Faith keeps you steadily walking forward, pursuing the Lord and His ways with diligence. Faith pleases God (see Hebrews 11:6). Where does faith come from? How can you grow in faith?

Choose four of the following verses and briefly note what they say about faith in the following chart. Try to include the scriptures marked with an asterisk (*). (If you are really adventurous, you can look them all up!)

Acts 15:9; Romans 1:17; *Romans 10:17; Galatians 2:20; Galatians 3:14; Ephesians 2:8; *Hebrews 11:1; James 2:17; 1 John 5:4

Scripture	What it Says About Faith

In light of the scriptures you just read, answer the following questions. How would you define Biblical faith?

How important is the Word to faith?

How do actions demonstrate faith?

The Bible says that faith is more than just thinking something is true. It is an active conviction that results in changed behavior—or obedience. When you have faith in God, you live differently. You make choices because of what you believe and live out those choices in confidence.

For example, the Bible says that Jesus will come again (see Acts 1:11). If you merely think about it, nothing really *changes*. But if you have faith in what He has said, then you will live in a way that shows it. Your actions will shout, "He's coming and I want to be ready!" You will seek Him, honor Him, and love Him—being fully committed to Him.

Similarly, if the Word says that God has set you free, then, your life choices should demonstrate your faith in what He has said. This is why we need to become faith-full people in order to press toward the goal. Believe what He has said and let your choices validate your belief in Him.

Romans 10:17 explains, "...faith comes by hearing, and hearing by the Word of God."

What one Bible verse has increased your faith in God this week? Write it here. You might consider also writing it on a note card to carry with you. You could review it and possibly commit it to memory. Take time to share the verse this week, telling someone how the Word has impacted your life.

Are you pressing toward the goal... Thank-full... Word-full... Faith-full?

Become a Spirit-full Person

Talk with a group of Christians about what it means to be "spirit-filled" and you are likely to get quite a variety of answers. Yet, the work of God in your life is dependent upon the Spirit of God touching your life. What does it mean, then, to be Spirit-full?

Ephesians 5:18 is a command. It says: "...Be filled with the Spirit."

In fact, the verb "be filled" could be written as "being filled." It is a continual action, not a one-time event. From this, you can begin to understand what is being said. God wants you to continually experience the touch of the Holy Spirit in your life. He wants you to everyday enjoy the strength, peace and blessing of His Spirit overflowing in you. As was asked in the teaching—are you "topped off?"

Match the following Bible verses with its corresponding statement about the Holy Spirit.

Titus 3:5	The Spirit gives life.
Romans 8:16	The Spirit guides to truth.
John 16:13	The Spirit renews.
1 Corinthians 2:10	The Spirit brings abounding hope.
John 6:63	The Spirit assures you that you are God's child.
Romans 15:13	The Spirit reveals the mysteries of God.

If you are going to press forward, you must do so in the power of the Holy Spirit. You must consciously lay down your thoughts, emotions and choices and invite the Holy Spirit to lead and guide, restore and renew just as He sees fit. You must lay down your life and receive His.

Be Spirit-full. Walk in the Spirit. Be led by the Spirit. Press forward—*by the Spirit!*

3.4 Become a Brand New Person

You have been given new life in Christ. You press toward the goal by learning to live out that new life through the power of the Holy Spirit. Growing in Christ is not a matter of will power; it is a matter of surrender. Salvation is a gift, and so is sanctification.

Read 2 Corinthians 5:17. According to this verse, what is gone?

What has come?

The new life God gives to you is not just a one-time event. He continually pours His power into you, to change you and make you more like His Son. This is the process of sanctification you learned about in the first Session. The new life God has given to you is *real* life. This is what the Bible means by being born again (see John 3:3). It is not just a new label that you wear; His life has enlivened you, and His Spirit dwells in you. Think about it: God lives in you. The same power that raised Jesus from the dead lives in you!

You have just walked through the Session teachings and the Retreat—where the worship, the truth, discipleship, and personal deliverance and healing ministry have brought greater freedom and wholeness to your soul. Often though, we do not realize the power of what has occurred, so our lifestyles do not change much.

Pressing forward means action. You pursue the Lord, and you allow His life to shine through your attitudes and actions. How? You pursue by *putting off* and *putting on*.

What You Put Off

Read the following scripture noting what has been crucified.

☐ Romans 6:6-7

☐ Galatians 5:24

Read the following scriptures and fill in the chart below noting what you are to put off and what you are to put on.

Scripture	Put Off	Put On
Ephesians 4:22-24		
Colossians 3:9-10		

To "put off" the sinful nature means that you do not give into actions or attitudes prompted by selfishness and pride; instead, you choose to respond to God and others through the guidance and empowering of the Holy Spirit.

The Scriptures that follow list the attitudes and actions that you are told to remove.

Ephesians 4:25, 31 (NIV) tells us, "Therefore each of you must put off falsehood (lying) and speak truthfully to his neighbor, for we are all members of one body... Get rid of all bitterness, rage and anger, brawling and slander, along with every form of malice."

Colossians 3:5, 8 says, "Therefore put to death your members which are on the earth: fornication, uncleanness, passion, evil desire, and covetousness, which is idolatry. But now you yourselves are to put off all these: anger, wrath, malice, blasphemy, filthy language out of your mouth."

Circle those things you need to purposefully put off.

How can you do this? You do this by thankfully and consistently submitting yourself to the truth of the Word of God. This is a process, and you must daily decide to walk in the Spirit. With bondage removed and healing received, the old way of living in those areas has been dealt a fatal blow, and you can now *make the choice* to live in ways that please the Lord. You are a brand new person—you are not the same person you were when you were first saved. You are not the same person who began the Seminar. You are not even the same person you were before attending the Retreat!

This does not mean that you will never struggle again. Every Christian does. The good news is that, through the power of God, you can daily invite His presence into your decisions and by faith, please Him in your choices. You can do this because you have grown and received freedom and healing in your soul. Even when your choices displease God, you can come to Him, repent, receive forgiveness and keep pressing toward the goal.

What You Put On

Putting off the actions and attitudes of your old ways is not enough. You need to put something on as well.

Looking back at Colossians 3:10, how is the new self renewed?

Colossians 3:12-14 lists the attitudes and actions you are to put on. Circle several that you desire to put on.

"Therefore, as the elect of God, holy and beloved, put on tender mercies, kindness, humility, meekness, longsuffering; bearing with one another, and forgiving one another, if anyone has a complaint against another; even as Christ forgave you, so you also must do. But above all these things put on love, which is the bond of perfection."

Ask the Lord to help you to walk in it.

Ephesians 5:8 says that though you were once in darkness, you are now to live as a child of light. Realize that this does not mean that you grit your teeth and in your own self-will decide to be kind and compassionate. It means that you acknowledge the work of grace God has done in you and the new life He gives you. You cultivate that life!

Galatians 5:1 (NIV) says, "It is for freedom that Christ has set us free. Stand firm, then, and do not let yourselves be burdened again by a yoke of slavery ("bondage" - NKJV)."

In addition to putting off and putting on, Galatians 5:1 tells you to do two things; underline them!

Why are these two things important?

3.5 Put Your House in Order

During Session Three you listened to an audio teaching which explored the idea of inviting God's presence on to your property and into your home. During this Session, you have been reading a book that gives practical guidelines on how you can do this. Both of these tools provide you a solid foundation and insight for this section. You will not need closet organizers or a dustpan, but you will need a sensitive spirit and a surrendered soul. Are you ready?

To continue to live in freedom, you must keep a watchful eye over your life. You must secure the spiritual boundaries of your life and your home. This means that you keep your borders intact, drawing a line between what is good and moves you toward God and what will only cause you to stumble again. Just as you watch over your soul to make sure that bitterness, fear and other harmful attitudes find no place to root, you must also watch over your relationships and home to see that there is no entrance for the enemy and his influence. Guard your souls *and* guard your family and home.

Read the following scriptures and note in the chart that follows, what the instructions are and to whom they are directed.

Scripture	Instructions	To Whom
Genesis 13:17		
Deuteronomy 11:24		
Joshua 1:3		

Notice that God promised to give them the land, but they had to "set their foot" on it. The land was theirs, but they needed to do something to actually possess it. The idea of God's people having to secure the land that He gave to them is sometimes used to explain the need for Christians to secure their "spiritual land" that God has given them. He has given you freedom, but you must possess it.

When you surrendered your life to the Lord and submitted yourself to the process of healing and restoration, He worked in you to cleanse and redeem. That work of the soul must now become a work of the hands. What does that mean? You must become attentive to what you keep in your house and carefully remove that which may be spiritually unhealthy. In other words, remove anything in your home that would allow an entrance of the enemy or influence of the flesh—anything that would introduce fear, idolatry, witchcraft, or any other influence of darkness. These can also be things—such as some secular music, inappropriate movies, books or magazines; "religious" artifacts, art pieces and anything that represents past sin or unhealthy relationships. In addition, consider the words, attitudes, or actions that take place in your home that do not honor the Lord. What you allow in your home must be that which builds up and bring glory to the Lord.

You did this for yourself when you identified areas in your life where past sin and bondage, hurts and wounds were restricting you from enjoying the full freedom God had for you, and you pursued your deliverance and healing! Now you need to do the same in your home. As you pray through your home, ask the Lord to reveal what needs to be cleansed or removed. He will reveal what is restricting your full freedom. Though the Bible does not give a list of what you can and cannot own, it does give guiding principles to assist in making wise choices.

Philippians 4:8 says, "Finally, brethren, whatever things are true, whatever things are noble, whatever things are just, whatever things are pure, whatever things are lovely, whatever things are of good report, if there is any virtue and if there is anything praiseworthy—meditate on these things."

Circle the types of things you should think about. How does this help you know what types of possessions you should have and the types of words and actions that should be in your home?

The Discipleship Assignment for *Press Toward the Goal* is to act on this teaching and literally cleanse your house as the Spirit leads you.

Prepare!
Review the homework materials previously mentioned to get an idea of what to do. Pray and ask the Lord to show you how to approach putting your house in order! Gather family and/or friends together. Have your Bible, oil for anointing and the communion elements (if you desire) available as needed. As you put your house in order be ready to pray, worship, walk, war, and possess your land!

Pray and ask the Lord to show you who you are to ask to pray with you and when you are to pray to possess your land. Record the "who" and the "when" and follow through to set it up.

5-31

Let's start *outside!*

Have you walked your property? If you have not, now is the time—if you have—maybe it is time to do it again. Just like dusting and weeding are ongoing necessities of maintaining a home, so walking, praying and possessing your property from the outside in is a spiritual necessity! This involves cleansing—removing physical and spiritual things that should not be in a place where the Lord dwells. Putting your house in order also involves covering—inviting and establishing God's rule. So, get your family or prayer partner and WALK! Record what the Lord revealed as you walked your property.

Then move *inside!*

Gather with your family or prayer partner to cleanse and cover the inside of your home. Ask the Lord to identify what—possessions, words, attitudes, actions—in your home do not honor Him. This is not to be done superstitiously or with any sense of eeriness or weirdness. It is simply a matter of cleansing your home to match the cleansing God has done in your soul. First, cleanse—repent and remove what is identified! Then cover—establish your home as a place set apart for the Lord—one where He is invited to rule and His Spirit feels comfortable dwelling. Record what the Lord revealed as you prayed through your home.

God has moved you from darkness to light (see Colossians 1:13), and He wants you to keep yourself in that light. Fill your home with possessions, words, attitudes and actions that inspire you to pursue the Lord. You are a brand new person—putting off and putting on.

So it is important to put your house in order—repenting and removing anything that does not please God and establishing His rule there!

3.6 Released to Serve

God has done so much in you over these past weeks. You are on the path to becoming all that God meant for you to be. Now the next step is to allow His work in you to spill over into the lives of others.

What God does in your life is never meant to be just a personal, individual experience. You are part of the Body of Christ—His Church. Sharing what God has done means that you live to serve others just as Jesus did. Through humbly serving, you allow His love and compassion to draw others to His heart.

Read Philippians 2:1-11. In what way is Jesus' life an example to us of how to treat others?

Mark 10:43-45 says "Yet it shall not be so among you; but whoever desires to become great among you shall be your servant. And whoever of you desires to be first shall be slave of all. For even the Son of Man did not come to be served, but to serve, and to give His life a ransom for many."

Circle the words relating to serving. What was the key to Jesus' ministry?

What will be the key to yours?

Ask the Lord to reveal an area of service in the Church you attend. Whatever His call is, answer it, pursue it with leadership, get involved in service. Write what the Lord revealed. Now follow through by submitting it to leadership.

Walking with the Lord by His Spirit is a journey. Each day is an opportunity to know God better and to extend His love to others. Take advantage of every moment. He is *with* you and He is *in* you.

How do you press toward the goal?

Continue the journey by becoming a *thank-full, Word-full, faith-full, Spirit-full* and a *brand new, cleansed* person... by putting your house in order through *cleansing* and *covering*... and by being *released to serve* with a humble heart!

Press Toward the Goal means to persevere in what the Lord has been teaching you through this Seminar and Retreat and to maintain the freedom and healing that has been received!

Joshua 3:14 through 4:4-7 records the miracle of the Israelites crossing the Jordan. They came from bondage and wanderings into their Promised Land and freedom. They took stones from inside the river—*the place of their miracle.* Then set them up as an altar of remembrance—*in the land of freedom and promise!* You can do the same so when others ask you what happened, you will have these "stones" to remind you of the miracles the Lord has done in your life during this season!

Build your altar of remembrance. Write down a revelation, a change, a freedom, a healing, or anything else significant that happened in your life because of the following...

*Seminar Teachings: Walk in the Spirit, Commit Everything to God, Speak Words of Life, Enter the Cleansing Stream, and Press Toward the Goal*_____

_____

_____

_____

*Homework: Workbook, Books, Audio Teachings*_____

_____

_____

_____

*Discipleship Assignments: Personal Bible reading—individually and out loud, personal devotional prayer and with a partner, fellowship with the Church and your Cleansing Stream Group, personal and family worship, fasting, putting on the armor, cleansing and covering your home*_____

_____

_____

_____

*Small Group: Encouragement and accountability*_____

_____

_____

_____

Retreat: _____

_____

_____

_____

Prayer
Commitment

As you begin this time of prayer and praise—let's review the theme verse of the Seminar. Read it out loud several times. Insert your name in each place where the word "you" appears.

Jeremiah 29:11 (NIV) says, "For I know the plans I have for (your name)," declares the Lord, "plans to prosper (your name) and not to harm (your name), plans to give (your name) hope and a future."

Then declare out loud, "I am being freed and healed to live the life God has planned for me!"

Psalm 100:4 (NIV) says, "Enter His gates with thanksgiving and His courts with praise; give thanks to Him and praise His name!"

Let thanksgiving flow out as a prayer to the Lord for all that He has done and will continue to do. Write it here as a reminder so when the enemy comes to steal your confidence and hope—you have truth to combat his lies! Hallelujah! _____

_____

_____

_____

Psalm 100:2 (NIV) says, "...come before Him with joyful songs."

End this time of building an altar with a song of praise—if you can't think of a song—make one up or open to the Psalms and come up with your own melody. The point is sing praise to Him—for He is worthy! Write down what you sang. _____

_____

Let what you wrote be an altar of His goodness that you can come back to and worship Him!

Signature_____ Date _____

CHUCK D. PIERCE
REBECCA WAGNER SYTSEMA

PROTECTING
YOUR HOME
FROM
SPIRITUAL
DARKNESS

Notes: _____
_____
_____
_____
_____
_____
_____
_____
_____
_____
_____
_____
_____

To Summarize:

Which truth had the greatest impact on you? _____
_____
_____

What was the most practical thing you learned? _____
_____
_____

How are you going to apply what you learned? _____
_____
_____

After the Seminar and Retreat

Christ has made us free—and completely liberated us—stand fast then, and do not be hampered, ensnared or submit again to a yoke of slavery—which you have put off. Galatians 5:1 (Amplified)

How do you stay free?

We invite you to go through again! This is a great way to solidify what you have learned as well as walk in the freedom and healing that you have received through the Seminar and Retreat.

We invite you to continue to grow! Your next time through the Seminar, check into the *Additional Homework Package.* (It includes a new book and audio teaching with new Bible Reading and Journaling Assignments.) Call us for information on this Additional Homework Package.

Whether you join us again or not, we pray that you may continue to, *...grow in the grace and knowledge of our Lord and Savior Jesus Christ. To Him be glory both now and forever! Amen.* 2 Peter 3:18

Cleansing Stream Ministries

Before Salvation: *Self-Rule*

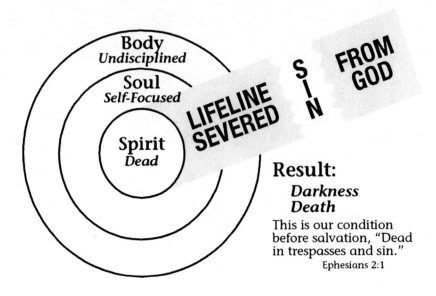

Body
Undisciplined

Soul
Self-Focused

Spirit
Dead

LIFELINE SEVERED   S I N   FROM GOD

Result:
Darkness
Death

This is our condition before salvation, "Dead in trespasses and sin."
Ephesians 2:1

After Salvation: *Jesus is Lord*

Body
Be Disciplined

Soul
Submitted to God

Spirit
Alive

RESTORED THROUGH ✝ CHRIST

Result:
Light
Life

This is our condition after salvation, "Reconciled to God in Christ."
2 Corinthians 5:18

Concept by Dr. Jack Hayford, used by permission.

FOREWORD BY JACK HAYFORD

CHRIS HAYWARD

GOD'S CLEANSING STREAM

Developing a Life-Changing
Deliverance Ministry in Your Church

Originally, deliverance was a part of the fabric of every local Church, but somewhere along the way the Church drew back from this vital ministry. The rise of humanism and secular self-help programs and the insistence of man's ability to change himself, edged the Church away from God's Word and power, often relegating deliverance to the superstitious and uninformed. Thankfully, God's Word does not change; His power does not diminish. Deliverance is His idea and He is restoring it to the Church!

This book provides a more complete picture of the vision of Cleansing Stream Ministries and removes roadblocks to the inclusion of the ministry of deliverance in the local Church.

Call Cleansing Stream Ministries today to order.

Have you have been blessed by the Seminar? Want to share it with your family? Cleansing Stream Ministries has the following packages available to do just that!

Cleansing Our Kids takes the Cleansing Stream Seminar Biblical principles and their application and puts them on a level that elementary age children can understand and apply. This package although designed for families to use in their homes has been easily adapted for use in a church or a classroom setting.

We, as parents make ensure that our children receive vaccinations and then booster shots. This package is like an immunization series against the plans of the enemy. Satan is looking to steal, kill, and destroy our children. But as we lay a foundation of godly principles for our children, we can prevent them from experiencing many of the disasters we have had to face in our lives.

Teen's Homework Package

Call for information on our Teen's Homework package for those under 16 going through the Cleansing Stream Seminar.

Call Cleansing Stream Ministries today to order.

Let's disciple a generation of those who love and obey the Lord and say "no" to sin and bondage.

CPSIA information can be obtained at www.ICGtesting.com
Printed in the USA
LVOW09s1335130214

373521LV00002B/2/P